THE World AND ITS People

Silver Burdett Ginn

Parsippany, NJ • Needham, MA

Atlanta, GA Deerfield, IL Irving, TX Santa Clara, CA

Silver Burdett Ginn
A Division of Simon & Schuster
299 Jefferson Road, P.O. Box 480
Parsippany, NJ 07054-0480

Developed and produced by
Small Planet Communications
Littleton, Massachusetts

3 4 5 6 7 8 9 10 B 05 04 03 02 01 00 99 98

2-32994-5

D1530559

CONTENTS

Name _____

Reading Population Density Maps

Understanding Population Density Maps

◇ Study the map below and answer the questions that follow.

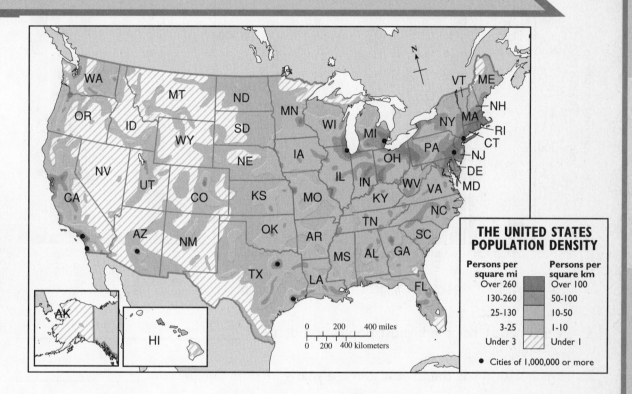

THE UNITED STATES POPULATION DENSITY

Persons per square mi	Persons per square km
Over 260	Over 100
130-260	50-100
25-130	10-50
3-25	1-10
Under 3	Under 1

● Cities of 1,000,000 or more

0   200   400 miles
0   200   400 kilometers

1. Which state has areas of higher population density, California or Alaska?

California

2. Does Nevada have a higher, or lower, population density than Ohio? lower

THINKING CRITICALLY: How would you describe where the most densely populated areas of the United States are to a person who had not seen this map?

Generally, the most densely populated areas are in the eastern part of the United States,

especially in the Northeast. The West Coast also has densely populated areas.

Chapter 1, pages 4–5

Name _____

Population Density and Income

Understanding Regional Economic Variations

◇ Study the bar graphs below and then answer the questions that follow.

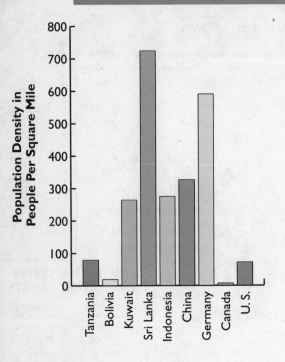

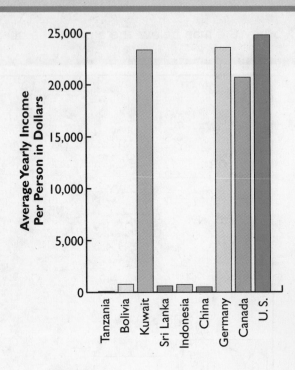

1. Which nation has the highest population density? Sri Lanka _____

2. Which nation has the lowest average yearly income per person? Tanzania _____

3. How do Kuwait and Indonesia compare in population density? Indonesia has a _____

slightly higher population density than Kuwait. _____

THINKING CRITICALLY: Is there a connection between a nation's population density and average yearly income per person? Explain your thinking after you have studied all the countries on the graph.

The graph shows that countries with a small population density can have either a high or a

low average yearly income per person. Countries with a high population density can also

show high or low average yearly incomes per person. So it is hard to make a general

connection between the two factors.

Name _____

World Climates

Understanding Stated Facts and Details

◇ Complete the chart with facts about the world's climates.
Sample answers are provided.

Type of Climate	Precipitation	Temperature	Sample Locations
Temperate	amount varies; snow and rain	warm in summer; cold in winter	United States, Europe, Asia
Tropical	**heavy rainfall; monsoons occur**	warm to hot all year round	Brazil, Zaire, Indonesia
Polar	snow most of the time	**cold all year round**	Antarctica, Greenland, Alaska
Dry	very little precipitation	varied: some very warm like deserts; some cooler	Africa, Middle East, Australia

THINKING CRITICALLY: How does climate create similarities in otherwise very different cultures? Give an example of two different cultures with similar climates.

Climate causes certain similarities among cultures such as clothing materials, types of food

eaten, and times of year that certain activities are done (for example, a festival marking the

end of a rainy season). Two cultures that have similar climates are people in the American

Southwest and people in central Australia.

_____

Name _____

What Is Geography?

Summarizing the Chapter

◇ Fill in the blanks in the chart below.

Ways of Identifying Regions

1. Climate What are the features that can make a climate region?

Temperature _____

Precipitation _____

2. Culture What are the features that can make a cultural region?

Language _____

Religion _____

Customs or traditions _____

Type of government _____

3. Landforms What physical features can make a landform region?

Mountains _____

River valleys _____

Plateaus _____

Plains _____

THINKING CRITICALLY: Think of the area that you live in. Identify it as part of two of the kinds of regions listed above. Give reasons for your answers.

Answers will vary but should reflect an understanding of the factors that are used to

identify various kinds of regions. _____

_____

_____

_____

Chapter 1, pages 6–15

Name _____

Comparing Time Lines

Comparing Time Lines

◇ Answer the following questions about the time lines below.

Events in the United States	**1775–1783** The War of Independence	**1783** Signing of the Treaty of Versailles	**1789** George Washington elected President	**1801** Thomas Jefferson became President
	1773 Boston Tea Party			

```
|       |       |       |       |       |       |       |
1750    1760    1770    1780    1790    1800    1810
```

Events in Great Britain	**1760–1783** Constitutional Crisis	**1783** Signing of the Treaty of Versailles	**1793–1815** War with France	**1800** Act of Union with Ireland

1. What periods of time do these time lines compare? 1773 to 1801 in the United

States; 1760 to 1800 in Great Britain

2. Which event is common to both time lines? Treaty of Versailles in 1783

3. Which two events end in the same year? The War of Independence and the

Constitutional Crisis

4. What was happening in Great Britain when Jefferson became President?

Great Britain was at war with France.

THINKING CRITICALLY: Would you say that the period on the time line was a peaceful time in the history of Great Britain? Explain your answer.

No. Great Britain was involved in America's War for Independence and later was at war

with France.

_____

ECONOMICS

Name _____

Economics Throughout History

CHAPTER 2

Understanding Economic Systems

◇ The complex economic systems of today grew out of the simple economic needs shared by all people. Answer the following questions about the role economy plays in the study of history.

1. Why did trade between people begin? Individuals and communities could not meet

all their needs and wants by themselves.

2. Why did trade grow? Trade grew because it helped those who engaged in it to thrive.

3. What effect did the law of supply and demand have on some countries? It helped

make some countries very wealthy.

4. How can economics be used to explain the history of a country? Some societies

became very powerful because they had strong economies.

5. Why have the economies of the world become so complex? Countries have

become increasingly dependent on trade with other countries.

THINKING CRITICALLY: In today's world there are many ways that people can "trade." Make a list of the different places and the different methods that you and your family use to trade for the goods you need.

Answers will vary but might include supermarkets, shopping malls, home shopping

networks, and catalog shopping.

Name _____

People Who Study People

Analyzing and Evaluating Information

◇ Complete the chart below that shows how people from different professions study the past, the problems they try to solve, and the work they do.

People	Problem	Work
Archaeologist	How to understand the past from the physical remains of societies	Digs at sites of old cities and villages
Anthropologist	How to understand the ways ancient people behaved	Studies human behavior
Paleontologist	How to understand what life was like in prehistoric times	Discovers and studies fossils of plants, animals, and humans
Geologist	How to understand the geography and climate of past civilizations	Studies soil and rock formations

THINKING CRITICALLY: Suppose that the professions listed above in the chart did not exist. Write what the study of history would be like without the knowledge these people provide.

Answers will vary.

_____

_____

_____

_____

Name _____

What Is History?

Summarizing the Chapter

◇ History combines information from different fields and different perspectives. Complete the chart below with details about these fields and perspectives. The first item in each box is provided for you.

Name four different kinds of history.
Social history
Oral history
Military history
Economic history

Name four kinds of people who help us to understand history.
Archaeologists
Anthropologists
Geologists
Paleontologists

HISTORY

Name four calendar systems.
Gregorian
Hebrew
Chinese
Islamic

Name four aspects of prehistoric life.
Pastoral migration
Cave painting
Stone tools
Religious celebrations

THINKING CRITICALLY: Explain why it is important to consider information from many different fields and perspectives when studying history.

Answers will vary but might indicate that the more information historians have from

different fields and perspectives, the better their understanding of the past will be.

_____

Name _____

The World We Live In

Here are some new things that I learned in this unit.

_____

_____

_____

_____

The most interesting thing I learned in this unit was _____

_____

_____.

My favorite activity in this unit was _____

_____

_____.

I think that another name for this unit could be _____

_____

_____.

Name _____

Reading Historical Maps

Understanding Historical Maps

◇ Study the map on page 55 and answer the questions that follow.

1. About how many miles did the Persian Empire stretch from east to west?

About 3,750 miles

2. Which seas were located on or within the boundaries of the Persian Empire?

Black Sea, Caspian Sea, Aral Sea, Arabian Sea, Mediterranean Sea, Persian Gulf, Red Sea

3. Describe what eventually happened to the area that was once the Persian Empire.

The area that was the Persian Empire became many different nations on three different

continents.

4. If you were asked to find out which modern nations are located in the area that was once Mesopotamia, how would you use the map on page 55?

I would compare the map on page 55 with a modern map of that area in order to figure

out which modern nations are located within Mesopotamia.

THINKING CRITICALLY: Compare and contrast the types of information provided by the maps on pages 50 and 55.

Both maps show the names of seas, ancient cities, and boundaries of regions of the past.

However, the map on page 50 provides information on the landscapes and geography of a

historical region. The map on page 55 shows boundaries of modern nations.

Chapter 3, pages 48–49, 50, 55

Trading and Culture

Understanding the Role of Trade

◇ **Answer these questions about trade in the Fertile Crescent.**

1. Who were the Phoenicians? These people lived in the Fertile Crescent and traded

and colonized along the coast and on islands of the Mediterranean Sea.

2. What were the home ports of the Phoenicians?

Byblos, Sidon, and Tyre were the home ports of the Phoenicians.

3. What were some places colonized by the Phoenicians?

They colonized Leptis, Carthage, Abdera, Majorca, and parts of Sardinia, Sicily, and Cyprus.

4. Why was the dye that the Phoenicians traded especially valuable?

The Phoenicans were the only ones who knew how to make it from sea snails.

5. What was the greatest and most lasting item the Phoenicians spread in their

trade? The most lasting item they spread was an alphabet much like the one we use today.

THINKING CRITICALLY: When people engage in worldwide trade today, what do
they spread around the world in addition to their goods?

They spread the culture of their own country. This includes knowledge and expertise,

music, clothing styles, vocabulary and language, art, customs, food, and technology.

Name _____

People of the Crescent

Understanding Stated Facts and Details

◇ In the blanks after the names below, explain the part each group played in the history of the region of the Fertile Crescent.

1. Sumerians

The Sumerians were among the first people in the region to build cities.

2. Babylonians

The Babylonians ruled after the Sumerians and established written laws.

3. Assyrians

The Assyrians were skilled warriors who conquered much of the Fertile Crescent.

4. Chaldeans

The Chaldeans defeated the Assyrians and rebuilt Babylon.

5. Persians

The Persians were outsiders who conquered the Chaldeans in 539 B.C.

6. Hebrews

The Hebrews built kingdoms on the Mediterranean coast of the Fertile Crescent.

THINKING CRITICALLY: To which of the groups listed above do we owe the most today? Explain your reasoning.

Answers will vary. Sample answer: We owe the most to the Sumerians because of their

many wonderful inventions, which include the wheel and writing.

Name _____

The Dawn of Civilization

Summarizing the Chapter

◇ Fill in the blanks in the chart to show what you know about how each of the following groups contributed to the dawning of civilization.

Mesopotamians

Location: Between the Tigris and Euphrates rivers

Means of Living: Farming, trading

Contribution: Writing, mathematics, the wheel, the plow

Phoenicians

Location: The Mediterranean seacoast and islands

Means of Living: Trading and seafaring

Contribution: The alphabet

Hebrews

Location: Canaan

Means of Living: Herding and farming

Contribution: Monotheism, the Ten Commandments

THINKING CRITICALLY: How would human history have been different if the Tigris and Euphrates rivers had not flowed through Mesopotamia?

Sample answer: The civilization of the Mesopotamians, which was based on successful

farming, would not have been able to develop. Other people in other favorable locations,

however, would certainly have made advances such as writing.

Name _____

A Cross Section

Making a Cross Section

◇ Some Egyptian pharaohs built their tombs inside the soft rock walls of valleys called wadis. In the space below, draw a cross section showing your design for a pharaoh's tomb.

THINKING CRITICALLY: Review your cross section. Is there any information missing? Add information to your cross section concerning the location of the tomb and the kind of room that would lead to the burial chamber.

Chapter 4, pages 70–71, 81

Egypt's Economy

Understanding Different Economies

◇ Answer each question about the economy of ancient Egypt.

1. What crops and animals did the Nile help support? The Nile supported wheat, barley, flax, cattle, pigs, goats, sheep.

2. How did the Egyptians use papyrus from the Nile? They used it for boats, baskets, ropes, and paper.

3. How did the middle class earn money? They earned money as physicians, artisans, soldiers, priestesses, weavers, perfume makers, musicians, and dancers.

4. What economic privileges did a woman have? A woman could own property and keep her dowry. A high-status woman might run her husband's business in his absence and was entitled to one third of her husband's property if they divorced.

5. How did agriculture help develop the sciences? Farmers needed to measure and calculate water volume to build canals and reservoirs, and surveyors needed mathematical skills to relocate dividing lines.

6. How did business help develop a system of writing? The practical need to keep records helped develop hieroglyphics.

THINKING CRITICALLY: You are a pharaoh in ancient Egypt. What changes would you make so that more people benefited from Egypt's wealth?

Answers will vary but should reflect an understanding of how the social structure of Egypt affected the economy.

Name _____

Notables of Ancient Egypt

Comparing, Contrasting, and Presenting Information

◇ The chart below gives information about some ancient Egyptians. Fill in the chart so that each person is named, described, and associated with a place and an event.

PEOPLE	DESCRIPTION	PLACES	EVENTS
Hyksos	Warriors	From the East	Conquered Lower Egypt
Imhotep	Vizier	Memphis	Built Step Pyramid
Wenu-hotep	Upper-class woman	Unknown	Was mummified
Piankhi	King of Kush	Kush, Heliopolis	Conquered Egypt
Hatshepsut	Stepmother of pharaoh	Deir el Bahri	Made herself pharaoh

THINKING CRITICALLY: Think about a person who had an impact on the ancient history of Egypt. Write a paragraph about that person from the point of view of a traveler who might have met him or her.

Answers will vary.
_____

_____

_____

_____

Name _____

The Egyptian Empire

Summarizing the Chapter

◇ Ancient Egyptian civilizations were highly advanced in many ways. Answer the questions in the chart. A few have been done for you.

Why was the Nile so important to ancient Egypt?

1. Provided water for irrigation

2. Transportation

3. Silt

4. Trade

How was the society of ancient Egypt structured?

1. Rulers or pharaohs

2. Nobles and priests

3. Skilled people and soldiers

4. Peasants and slaves

In what areas were important contributions made by ancient Egyptians?

1. Building pyramids and monuments

2. Mathematics/Geometry

3. Medicine

4. Hieroglyphics

THINKING CRITICALLY: Think about how a person's life in ancient Egypt was affected by his or her social class. Suppose you are a boy or girl from one of those social classes. Write a paragraph describing your life as a child and as an adult.

Answers will vary.

_____

_____

_____

_____

Name _____

Reading Special-Purpose Maps

Understanding Special-Purpose Maps

◇ The special-purpose map below shows precipitation in Sri Lanka, an island nation off the coast of India. Study it and answer the questions that follow.

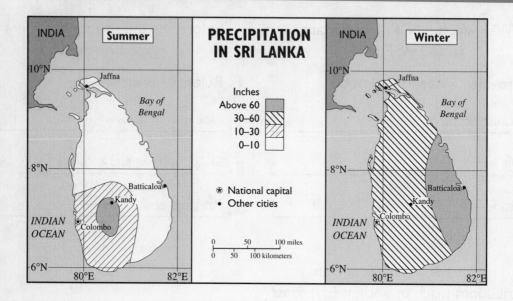

1. How does precipitation in Colombo vary from summer to winter?

In summer the precipitation is between 10 and 30 inches. In winter it is between 30 and

60 inches.

2. During which season is the precipitation in Sri Lanka greater? How can you tell?

Precipitation is greater in the winter. The larger amount of shading and hatching on the

winter map shows this.

THINKING CRITICALLY: If you had to live in either Kandy or Batticaloa, which city would you choose if you wanted the one with less precipitation?

Batticaloa. Both receive more than 60 inches in one season. However, Kandy receives

between 30 and 60 inches in the other season, while Batticaloa receives less than 10 inches.

Name _____

Economics and Ethics

Making Ethical Judgments About Economics

◇ Read the paragraph below and answer the questions that follow.

Economics is the study of money and how it works in society. Ethics is the study of what is right and wrong. What happens when economics and ethics clash? You read how Jains in ancient India believed that they should not farm because they might kill small creatures living in the soil. As a result, many Jains became merchants. For them, ethics affected economics. Today some people are concerned that some products Americans buy are made in countries where factories are dangerous or unhealthy. They worry that foreign workers are not paid enough to live healthy, happy lives. But others say that by buying foreign goods, Americans give foreign workers jobs they would not otherwise have.

1. Why did many Jains become merchants? They became merchants in order to avoid

farming, which required killing small creatures in the soil.

2. How do economics and ethics clash today? Some products that Americans buy are

made in countries where factories are dangerous or unhealthy.

THINKING CRITICALLY: Suppose you found out that some sneakers you wanted to buy were made in another country by a person your age. That young person works in a factory twelve hours a day, seven days a week, for very little money. Would you buy the sneakers? Why or why not?

Answers will vary. Some students may indicate that they would refuse to buy the sneakers

because they do not want to encourage the use of child labor; others may indicate that

they would buy the sneakers in order to provide the child worker with a livelihood.

Name _____

Key Places in Ancient India

Identifying Landforms and Bodies of Water

◇ Study the map below and the map on page 94 in your textbook. Then answer the questions that follow.

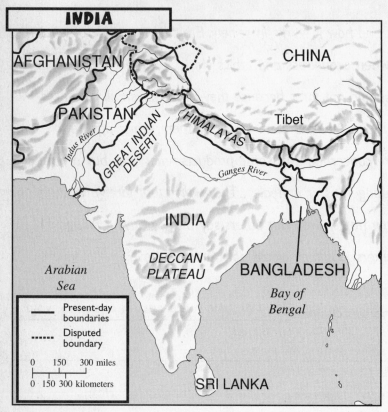

INDIA

AFGHANISTAN

PAKISTAN

CHINA

Tibet

Indus River

GREAT INDIAN DESERT

HIMALAYAS

Ganges River

INDIA

DECCAN PLATEAU

BANGLADESH

Arabian Sea

Bay of Bengal

— Present-day boundaries

----- Disputed boundary

0   150   300 miles

0 150 300 kilometers

SRI LANKA

1. In what modern nations is the site of the great Indus Valley civilizations?

The Indus Valley civilization

was located in what is now

Pakistan and India.

2. The southern part of India was never conquered by the Aryans. What makes it a separate region? The Deccan

Plateau makes southern India a

separate region.

3. What natural features helped protect ancient Indian civilization from invasion?

The Himalayas to the north and the Great Indian Desert to the west protected India from

invasion.

THINKING CRITICALLY: Monsoons are caused by differences in the heating and cooling of air over land and water. How does India's location contribute to the monsoons?

India is a peninsula that is surrounded by the Arabian Sea and the Bay of Bengal. The

presence of water on each side makes India vulnerable to the winds that arise over the

open water.

Name _____

Empires of Ancient India

Summarizing the Chapter

◇ Fill in the chart below by summarizing the culture of each group listed.
Sample answers are provided.

GROUP	WHAT ITS CULTURE WAS LIKE
The People of the Indus Valley	These people used bronze tools, lived in houses of baked mud bricks, and wore cotton clothes.
The Aryans	The Aryans came from beyond the Hindu Kush. They spoke Vedic, used horses to pull fast chariots, and were herders who gradually began to farm.
The Maurya	The Maurya counted perhaps 50 million people with different languages and religions in their wealthy empire.
The Gupta	The Gupta marked a high point in Indian culture during which the arts and learning in science and medicine flourished.
The Chola	The Chola lived in southern India. Their ruler Rajendra built a powerful navy that helped create routes by which Indian culture spread.

THINKING CRITICALLY: Describe one way in which the learning or beliefs of ancient India affect you today.

Answers will vary. Sample answer: The use of so-called arabic numerals has made possible

much of the technology that affects my everyday life.

Name _____

Reading a Process Diagram

Understanding Diagrams

◇ Below are six steps in how to paint a bicycle. Write the steps in sequence above each box. Draw pictures in the boxes to complete the process diagram.

- Reassemble all the hardware you took off.
- Scrub rust off frame with steel wool.
- Paint the frame with primer.
- Have your bike shop check your bike for safety.

- Remove all hardware you are not going to paint.
- When the primer is dry, paint the frame with a finish coat.

Remove all hardware you are not going

to paint.

1.

Scrub rust off frame with steel wool.

2.

Paint the frame with primer.

3.

When the primer is dry, paint the frame

with a finish coat.

4.

Reassemble all the hardware you took off.

5.

Have your bike shop check your bike for

safety.

6.

THINKING CRITICALLY: What is the most important step in the process diagram above? Explain your answer.

The most important step in the process diagram is having the bike checked for safety

after it has been painted. Unless this step is taken, the bike may not be safe to use.

_____

Name _____

Commerce in a Chinese City

ECONOMICS

CHAPTER 6

Understanding the Role of Trade

◇ People who lived in or visited the ancient city of Hangzhou could see and buy many things. Some people who might have been there describe themselves below. On the blank lines, tell what each person might have bought or seen.

1. "My daughter wants me to make her a beautiful wedding dress." Silk _____

2. " I have just become a grandparent." A child's toy _____

3. "I need something to keep my mind busy now that I am too old to work."

A printed book _____

4. "I make jewelry boxes." Rare and fragrant woods _____

5. "I'm very hungry after my long trip to the city!"

Tea and foods such as chicken, goose, pigeon, lamb, and shellfish _____

6. "I'm bored and would like to be entertained."

A show from martial arts experts, jugglers, puppeteers, dancers, comedians, or

snake charmers. _____

THINKING CRITICALLY: What would Hangzhou have been like without trade? Is it possible for a city to exist without trade?

Sample answer: Hangzhou would have been a much less interesting and attractive place.

Cities probably cannot exist without some kind of trade among their inhabitants, because

city dwellers generally depend upon food grown by others or by a limited number of

people.

_____

Chapter 6, pages 124-125

25

Name _____

Personalities of Ancient China

Understanding Stated Facts and Details

◇ **Answer the following questions about various people of Ancient China.**

1. Who was the First Emperor? He was a ruler of the Qin dynasty whose name was

Shi Huang Di.

2. What did Confucius teach? Confucius taught that people should treat others as they

wished to be treated and that moral education would show people how to act correctly.

_____

3. What philosophy did Laozi found, and what did it teach? He founded Daoism.

It taught that people should escape from society and retreat into nature.

4. Why is Liu Bang famous today? He became the first ruler of the Han dynasty in

206 B.C.

5. Why was Wu Zhao an unusual emperor of China? She was the only female emperor

in Chinese history.

THINKING CRITICALLY: Song Emperor Hui Zong supported arts such as paint-
ing and pottery making. Do you believe governments should pay money to
support the arts? Explain.

Answers will vary. Sample answer: I believe that governments should not support the arts

because government should provide only a very few vital services such as defense.

_____

_____

Dynasties of Ancient China

Summarizing the Chapter

◇ Fill in the chart by listing examples from the chapter beside each heading.

	Ancient China
Beliefs	China is the center of the world. China is superior to other lands. Harmony is very important. The Three Teachings—Confucianism, Daoism, and Buddhism—all fulfill different needs.
Dynasties	The Shang (1766–1222 B.C.)　　　The Qin (221–206 B.C.) The Han (206 B.C.–618 A.D.)　　　The Tang (A.D. 618–960) The Song (960–1279)
Inventions	Silk cloth　　　　　　　　　Printing Paper money　　　　　　　Navigation tools

THINKING CRITICALLY: The building of the Great Wall of China is said to have cost a million Chinese lives. Was the wall worth it? Explain your thoughts.

Answers will vary. Sample answer: I think that the cost is acceptable if the wall really saved

millions of lives. Or: I think the cost is unacceptable because the loss of so many lives

shows that proper safety precautions were not taken or that the workers were not well

cared for.

Name _____

Using Primary and Secondary Sources

Using Primary and Secondary Sources

◇ Answer the questions about primary and secondary sources.
Sample answers are provided.

1. List three examples each of primary sources and secondary sources.

Primary: artifact, letter, news report

Secondary: history book, article, documentary film

2. Find a primary source mentioned in the chapter. What is it, and what facts does it

reveal about the past? The gold funeral mask thought to be Agamemnon reveals that the

Mycenaeans performed funeral rites or had ceremonies for the dead and that there was

gold in their lands.

3. If you were a historian of ancient Greece, why might you travel to Athens?

I might travel to Athens because there are many primary sources there in museums as well

as architectural ruins to look at.

THINKING CRITICALLY: You are a historian writing a magazine article about
how democracy in Greece has changed from ancient Athens to the present
day. What kinds of primary and secondary sources would you use for your
research?

Answers will vary, but may include legal documents, letters and memoirs by politicians and

ordinary citizens, history books, news articles and newsreels, and the buildings in which

leaders met. Students should distinguish between primary and secondary sources.

Name _____

The Power of Trade

Understanding the Relationship Between Geography and Trade

◇ Greece's geography contributed to its rise to power. Answer the questions below.

1. What geographic feature of Greece made it suitable for trade? Greece has access to large bodies of water since it has a peninsula and many islands, so travel by sea was easy.

2. Why did Greece depend on trade so much? Agriculture was difficult there because the water supply was often low, and as the population grew, there was a shortage of fertile land.

3. Describe trade between Greece and other parts of the world. Olive oil, woolen cloth, perfumes, and metalware were shipped from Crete to Asia, Africa, and Europe. Athens imported grain from its Asian colonies. Ships also returned to Greece with gold and pearls from Egypt and tin from Persia.

4. Why was Crete a "natural trading center"? Crete was a natural trading center because it was an island and it was located in a strategic place on the edge of the Mediterranean, making trade with Asia, Europe, and Africa easy.

THINKING CRITICALLY: How might the history of Greece have been different if it had not consisted of so many islands?

Sample answer: It would not have had natural protection, such as the island of Crete had, from enemies or invaders. This would have reduced its ability to trade and prevented Greece from building such a powerful civilization.

Chapter 7, pages 138–143

Name _____

Who's Who in Ancient Greece

Understanding Stated Facts and Details

◇ Create a directory of important people in ancient Greece. Fill in the chart with information about where each person could be found and what he or she did. The first row has been completed for you. Sample answers are provided.

Person	Place	Occupation
Alexander the Great	Macedonia	Taking over power in Greece and conquering the Persian Empire
Sappho	Greece	Writing poetry about love, friendship, and joy
Pericles	Athens	Developing systems of law and democracy in Greece
Apollo	Temple at Delphi	Giving advice to people
Sophocles	Theater	Writing plays

THINKING CRITICALLY: Compare and contrast the Athenians and the Spartans.

The Athenians and the Spartans were both citizens of powerful city-states in ancient

Greece. They spoke the same language. The Spartans were more concerned with training

their citizens to be warriors, starting with very young boys. Athenians were concerned

with war, but they also developed other aspects of their society, such as socializing

in the agora, enjoying plays and music, and studying philosophy and science.

Chapter 7, pages 138–157

Name _____

Civilizations of Ancient Greece

Summarizing the Chapter

◇ Fill in the web below by listing three contributions made by ancient Greece in each category.

ARTS

dramatic plays

sculptures, especially of human body

ornate columns and buildings

GOVERNMENT

city-state—among first organized societies

Athenian democracy (Solon)

jury system (Pericles)

Greek Contributions

EDUCATION

philosophy (Plato and Socrates)

mathematics, such as Euclid's geometry

advances in medicine (Hippocrates)

MILITARY

Philip II's military tactics

The Battle of Troy—popular war legend

Military victories by Athens inspired the

Golden Age.

THINKING CRITICALLY: What do you think will happen after the fall of Athens to the Spartans? What evidence in past history supports your prediction?

Sample answer: The city-state of Sparta will dominate the Greek peninsula, conquer more

lands, and develop a greater society. This would follow the pattern of when Athens came to

power by military victory and then flourished.

★ **SKILL POWER**

Name _____

Comparing Maps

Comparing Maps

◇ Compare the current map below with the map on page 168 of your book in order to answer the questions that follow.

EUROPE AND THE MEDITERRANEAN IN 1996

1. In which region of the former Roman Empire is the modern country of Algeria located? _Algeria is located in what was once Mauritania._

2. What is the major difference between the map on page 168 and the map above?

The map on page 168 shows different areas of the Roman Empire.

The current map shows many independent countries.

THINKING CRITICALLY: Think of some reasons why boundaries on maps are changed. List the reasons below.

Sample answers: New lands are discovered and claimed. One country takes over another's

territory during war. Governments collapse and countries either reunite or divide along

ethnic lines.

Chapter 8, pages 162–163, 168

Name _____

Mediterranean Marketplace

Understanding Economic Events

◇ Answer these questions about the economy of the ancient Roman Empire.

1. What building projects did the Romans undertake to maintain their wealth?

They built a network of paved roads, as well as a system of aqueducts.

2. What did the Romans do in order to expand their empire? They invaded

neighboring countries, conquered them, and ruled over their people.

3. How did the Roman emperors use their wealth to keep their citizens happy?

They gave away free food, such as bread and meat, and provided free entertainment

at the Circus Maximus and the Colosseum.

4. How were the many cultures under the Roman Empire reflected in its daily life?

In the Forum, there were merchants from all corners of the empire selling their goods.

5. What economic needs drove Germanic people to wage war against the Roman

Empire? As their population grew, the Germanic people needed more land for farming.

THINKING CRITICALLY: Despite centuries of prosperity, the Roman Empire collapsed. Give some reasons that led to the collapse.

Sample answer: Later emperors chosen by the army were not able rulers. Central authority

broke down, roads were not maintained, and outer provinces began to break away.

Germanic peoples eventually invaded Italy and forced the last Roman emperor to resign.

Name _____

Romans and Countrypeople

Understanding Stated Facts and Details

◇ The boxes below list people, real or fictional, connected with the Roman Empire. Fill in the blanks with information about places and events related to each person. Sample answers are given.

Person	A Roman girl
Places	the home, school
Events	arranged marriage, runs household after marriage

Person	A Roman father
Places	the home
Events	ruled the household

Person	Octavian
Places	battle of Actium
Events	defeated Antony's fleet

Person	Hannibal
Places	Carthage, the Alps
Events	crossed the Alps and tried to conquer Rome in 218 B.C.

THINKING CRITICALLY: Suppose you are a reporter who is going to interview one person listed above. Write the name of that person. Then list three questions you would ask in your interview.

Answers will vary. _____

_____

_____

Name _____

The Heritage of Rome

Summarizing the Chapter

◇ Roman culture was shaped by many factors, and in turn had a profound influence on later cultures. Complete the chart below.

1. Which physical characteristics of the Italian peninsula affected the ancient Romans?

The Alps

The Tiber and Po rivers

The Adriatic, Ionian, and Tyrrhenian seas

_____

2. What inequalities characterized the Roman Republic?

Two social classes divided the people.

Women couldn't vote or hold office.

Plebeians paid taxes but could not hold

public office.

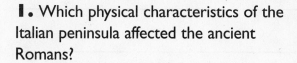
ROME

3. How did Christianity grow under the Roman Empire?

Christianity, founded on the teachings of

Jesus, was spread by his disciples.

Constantine declared religious freedom

for Christians. Theodosius made

Christianity the official religion of the empire.

4. What did Roman culture contribute to other societies?

Law and government

Language

Architecture and building

_____

_____

THINKING CRITICALLY: Write a dialogue between a patrician, who wants to keep plebeians out of power, and a plebeian who wants to gain political power.

Answers will vary.

_____

_____

Name _____

Ancient Times

This is what I learned about ancient civilizations in this unit.

_____

_____

_____

_____

_____

Now I can locate these places on a map.

_____

_____

_____

_____

I'd like to learn more about _____

_____ because

_____

_____.

Name _____

Making Inferences

Making Inferences

◇ Read the passages below. Then make inferences about the passages and tell what clues you used.

1. "Johannes, you are a genius for having built this machine! Scholars from all over Europe will benefit. More people will be able to read information in books."

Who is Johannes and what did he build? Johannes Gutenberg built a printing press.

Clues: built a machine, scholars benefit, read information in books

2. Though she was born a peasant, she went on to great achievements. She was acclaimed throughout France for liberating her country. In the end she was held by her witch-hunting enemies and suffered the burning death.

Whom is the passage about? Joan of Arc

Clues: peasant, liberated her country

How did she die? She was burned at the stake.

Clues: witch-hunting enemies, burning death

THINKING CRITICALLY: Choose a person or event described in Chapter 9. Write a passage that implies who the person or event is but doesn't state it directly. Switch papers with a partner and make inferences about the person or event described.

Answers will vary.

_____
_____
_____

SKILL POWER

CHAPTER 9

Chapter 9, pages 190–191, 203, 204

Name _____

Feudalism and Its Decline

Understanding Economic Systems

◇ Answer the following questions.

1. Explain the relationships between kings, lords, knights, and serfs.

Kings were leaders of all the land. Lords owned a lot of land but were vassals to the King.

Knights were vassals to the lords and were given manors. Serfs had no land of their own

and worked on the manors.

2. What work did serfs do on the manors? They raised what they needed, grew food,

raised animals for food and wool, and managed trees in the forest for fuel and lumber.

3. Why was there very little trade during feudalism?

The manors were self-sufficient.

4. What happened to trade as towns began to revive? Trade increased as people

moved back to towns; the towns became centers of learning, art, and commerce,

5. Why did the growth of towns and increase in trade lead to the end of feudalism?

With trade, towns began to prosper, so peasants, lesser nobles, scholars, and others began

to move to the towns.

Thinking Critically: If you lived during the Middle Ages, would you prefer to live in a town or on a manor? Why?

Answers will vary.

_____

_____

_____

Name _____

Events of Note

Understanding Stated Facts and Details

◇ Complete the chart with events, people, and places from Chapter 9.

EVENT	PERSON	PLACE
Justinian Code	Emperor Justinian	Byzantine Empire
becomes Emperor of the Holy Roman Empire	Charlemagne	France; Switzerland; Belgium; the Netherlands; parts of Italy, Germany, and Spain
begins the Crusades	Pope Urban II	Europe and Middle East
Norman duke conquers England	William the Conqueror	England
becomes queen of two countries	Eleanor of Aquitane	France/England
signs Magna Carta	King John	England
peasant leads armies	Joan of Arc	France
creates printing press	Johannes Gutenberg	Mainz, Germany

THINKING CRITICALLY: Which of the events above had the most influence over European society in the Middle Ages? Explain your opinion.

Answers will vary. Sample answer: The Magna Carta was most important because it

required the king to obey the laws of the land. It helped to reform the legal system and set

up some rights and liberties for the English people.

_____

Name _____

Byzantium and Medieval Europe

Summarizing the Chapter

◇ **For each lesson, write a sentence that gives the main idea. Then write a brief summary of the chapter.** Sample answers are provided.

Lesson	Summary Sentence
1. Byzantine Empire and Medieval Europe	Many European traditions are rooted in cultural traditions from the Byzantine Empire and medieval society.
2. People and Events	In the Middle Ages people accomplished a lot, but there were also problems with Viking raids, and many people died during the black plague.
3. The Flourishing of Culture	Education, art, architecture, and literature all flourished during the Middle Ages.
4. Children's Lives	Working-class children were apprenticed. Children of the nobility were trained in their duties. People often married young.
5. Your Place in the Castle	Castles were walled enclosures where hundreds of people lived and worked.

Chapter Summary:

The cultural traditions of Western Europe came out of the Byzantine Empire and medieval society. Education, art, architecture, and literature began to flourish, but there were many setbacks because of Viking raids and the black plague. Walled fortresses such as castles helped to protect people. Childhood was short and people married and began work at an early age.

THINKING CRITICALLY: What do you think was the most exciting part of life in medieval Europe? What would you have liked to be part of?

Answers will vary. _____

_____

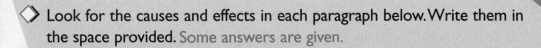

Understanding Cause and Effect

Identifying Cause-and-Effect Relationships

◇ Look for the causes and effects in each paragraph below. Write them in the space provided. Some answers are given.

1. Arabia's importance increased in the sixth and seventh centuries because the Persian and Byzantine empires were at war. The fighting disrupted the trade routes to the north, and more merchants started to send their wares through Arabia.

Cause:

The Persian and Byzantine empires were at war.

Effect:

The fighting disrupted trade routes to the north.

Effect:

More merchants sent their wares through Arabia.

2. In 732, at a day-long battle near the city of Tours, the Muslims were defeated by an army led by Charles Martel. This was a very important battle in world history. Martel's victory meant that most of Europe would remain Christian.

Cause:

The Muslims were defeated in 732 by an army led by Charles Martel.

Effect:

Most of Europe remained Christian.

3. Far to the east, the Arabs defeated the Chinese in 751 at the battle of Talas, in central Asia. This too was a decisive battle. The Chinese empire would never again reach that far west, and Islam replaced Buddhism as the major religion of central Asia.

Cause:

The Arabs defeated the Chinese in 751 at the battle of Talas.

Effect:

Islam replaced Buddhism as the major religion of central Asia.

THINKING CRITICALLY:
Why is it important for historians to understand not only the effects of past events but also the causes of those events?

Historians must be able to determine both what happened and why it happened. Without

knowing why a certain event happened, history would be a series of unanswered questions.

Name _____

Shopping in Baghdad

Understanding Stated Facts and Details

◇ Suppose you are a merchant in eighth century Baghdad. You own a shop filled with imported and locally-made goods. Answer the questions below based on your viewpoint as a shopkeeper.

1. What goods might you stock on your shelves? Where would these items and foods come from? Foods might include locally-produced rice, sugar cane, lemons, limes, bananas, coconuts, spinach, and eggplant. Other goods include porcelain from China, ivory and gold from Africa, and furs from northern Europe.

2. How would your business have been influenced by each of the following?

Warfare between Persians and Byzantines War between Persians and Byzantines increased Arabia's importance as a trade route and would have improved a Baghdad merchant's business.

The desire to spread Islam As Islam spread, new trade routes opened. Now a merchant could obtain more goods from distant places.

THINKING CRITICALLY: How would the work of Muslim scientists on the compass, the astrolabe, and on tides and winds have been beneficial to a shopkeeper in Baghdad?

These new instruments and information about tides and winds enabled navigators to cross the oceans to China, Africa, and other lands. There they could obtain exotic goods to be sold. Such a supply of goods would help a shopkeeper expand his offerings and interest more customers in his wares.

Chapter 10, pages 220–225, 230

Name _____

Exploring the World of Islam

Understanding Main Ideas

◇ Some people, places, and events in the world of Islam are described in the boxes below. Identify each person, place, or event on the line provided.

People	Places	Events
These rulers became known as Allah's "shadow on earth." Abbassid caliphs	Muhammad left Mecca and went to this city in 622. Medina	This pilgrimage to Mecca is the fifth pillar of Islam. hajj
These Muslims sought to become closer to God through meditation, fasting, and a simple life. Sufis	Near this city, a Christian army defeated the Muslims and stopped their advance into Europe. Tours	A disagreement about the leadership of the caliphs resulted in these two groups of Muslims. Sunnite and Shi'i
This man united the Muslim armies to capture Jerusalem. Saladin	An Abbassid caliph built this on the Tigris River. Baghdad	The first of these opened in Baghdad and sold medicines, tonics, and ointments. pharmacy

THINKING CRITICALLY: How might some of the teachings of Islam have helped Muslims conquer such a vast amount of territory?

Islam's message that all believers were equal in the eyes of Allah helped to mend the

differences that had split Arabs into warring communities. They then had the strength to

conquer other lands. In addition, Muslim soldiers were fearless in battle, because Islam

taught them that if they died, they would be carried into paradise.

Name _____

The World of Islam

Summarizing the Chapter

◇ Fill in the information in the chart below.

Chapter 10 Title: The World of Islam _____

Main Ideas/Topics:

After Muhammad's death, the followers of Islam created a powerful empire. Both the

Islamic religion and Muslim culture spread from Arabia to Europe, Africa, and the rest

of Asia.

Important Events:

Sample answers include: warfare between Persians and Byzantines; Muhammad's migration from Mecca to Medina (Hijrah); Battle at Tours in 732; Muslim defeat of the Chinese at the Battle of Talas in 751; bringing of new food crops to the Middle East from India; the Crusades; the opening of the first pharmacies; the perfecting of the compass and the astrolabe.

Important People:

Students should include: Al-Battani, Al-Biruni, Ibn Sina, Al-Razi, Al-Idrisi, Omar Khayyam, Muawiya, Saladin, Ibn Battuta, Muhammad, Abu-Bakr, Al-Mansur, Al-Kwarizmi

THINKING CRITICALLY: Explain why this is an incorrect statement: After an army led by Charles Martel won a battle near Tours in 732, the Muslim empire was weakened and never recovered from that defeat.

The statement is incorrect because the Muslim empire continued after this battle

for several hundred years. During this time, the city of Baghdad was built, trade flourished,

magnificent palaces were built, and science and art made great strides.

Name _____

Using a World Atlas

Understanding Special-Purpose Maps—Resource Maps

◇ Use the resource map of Africa below to answer the following questions.

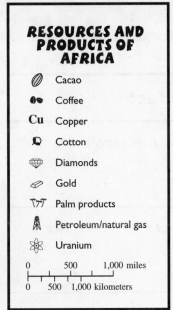

RESOURCES AND PRODUCTS OF AFRICA

⬭ Cacao
☕ Coffee
Cu Copper
🗇 Cotton
💎 Diamonds
▱ Gold
⑂ Palm products
🛢 Petroleum/natural gas
⚛ Uranium

0   500   1,000 miles
0   500   1,000 kilometers

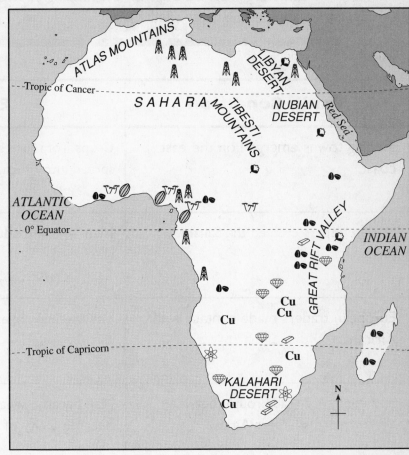

1. Near which desert would you find uranium?

the Kalahari Desert
_____

2. Where are palm products made? in western Africa, above the equator
_____

3. What is the major resource in northern Africa? petroleum/natural gas
_____

THINKING CRITICALLY: Based on the resources shown on the map, what kinds of job opportunities do you think are available in Africa?

Sample answer: Jobs in agriculture, mining, drilling for oil and natural gas, transportation
_____

and shipping
_____

_____

Name _____

Trade in Africa

Understanding the Effects of Trade on the Economy

◇ Over the centuries, trade and the contact it brought with foreign cultures had a profound impact on African cultures. Complete the graphic organizer below with the missing information about trading conditions and their effects.

Trade Condition	Effect
Trading towns emerged on the east coast.	Crops from Asia, such as yams and taro, spread into Africa.
Muslim traders crossed the Sahara.	Islam was introduced to West Africa.
European traders made contact with Africans.	The trade in slaves began.
Mali controlled trade routes between northern and southern Africa.	Mali became wealthy and Timbuktu became a city of learning.

THINKING CRITICALLY: List the different ways in which Africa's climate and geography have affected its economy.

Answers will vary but should mention the crops that can be grown in Africa; the effects of

rain, wind, and drought on crops; the natural resources in Africa, such as gold; its coastline;

and its proximity to Asia and India.

Chapter 11, pages 242–249, 255

People of Africa

Understanding Facts and Details; Analyzing Influences

◇ **Answer these questions about people and culture in African civilizations.**

1. Why are griots important in some African cultures?

Griots preserve in memory the customs, traditions, and laws of their people.

_____

2. Why does the word *Bantu* occur in so many African languages?

When Africans who spoke Bantu migrated to other regions, their language influenced other

languages.

3. How did Mansa Musa change the culture of Mali?

He went to Mecca and brought Muslim scholars back to Mali.

4. What are three outward signs of adulthood in some African cultures?

Raised scars, new hair style, clothing and jewelry

5. How did Askia Muhammad's religious beliefs affect Songhai?

He formed his government according to Muslim law.

THINKING CRITICALLY: Either directly or indirectly, African culture has affected
the lives of all Americans. How have you been affected by African culture?

Answers will vary.

_____

_____

_____

Name _____

Africa South of the Sahara

Summarizing the Chapter

◇ Write two facts to support the statement in each box.
Sample answers are provided.

Geography and Climate
Environmental conditions have helped shape African cultures.

In some regions seasons are determined by rainfall rather than temperature.

The drying of the Sahara region forced people into other regions.

Civilizations
Africa is made up of a variety of cultural traditions.

Islam has been an important influence in some regions.

The Bantu migration spread the Bantu language and culture across Africa.

Cultural Influence
African musical culture has had an international impact.

Some spiritual music has its roots in the songs brought from Africa.

Jazz grew out of the improvisational element of African music.

THINKING CRITICALLY: Suppose you lived in a village in Africa. Explain what you would like best about life in your clan.

Answers will vary.

_____

_____

_____

Chapter 11, pages 242–257

Using Scale to Compute Travel Time

Understanding Scale; Using Scale to Measure Distance

◇ On the map below, use a piece of string and the map scale to find the distances Marco Polo traveled between the listed cities. Then determine the number of days traveled by assuming that Marco Polo could travel 20 miles a day over land. Finally, add the travel times together to arrive at the total travel time.

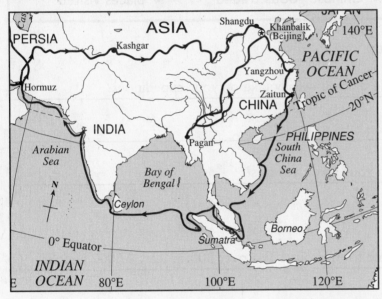

MARCO POLO'S JOURNEY

✳ Imperial city

• Other cities

→ Marco Polo's route

0   500   1,000 miles

0   500   1,000 kilometers

Thinking Critically:

A traveler must think ahead when planning a trip. What parts of a trip would knowing travel time help you plan?

It is essential to know travel time to plan how long to allow for the trip, when you must stop for gasoline, how long before you can find food along the way, how long before you find a restroom, and whether you will need a hotel room for the night.

	Miles	Travel Time
From Hormuz to Kashgar	1,625	81-1/4 days
From Kashgar to Shangdu	2,400	120 days
From Shangdu to Khanbalik	200	10 days
From Khanbalik to Pagan	1,750	87-1/2 days
From Yangshou to Zaitun	500	25 days
Total Travel Time:		323-3/4 days

Name _____

Trading in Faraway Lands

Understanding Trade

◇ Suppose you are a newspaper reporter investigating the economic aspects of the seven voyages of Zheng He. Using the topics below, write questions you might ask Zheng He during an interview. Then write the response you think Zheng He would give to each question.

Interview Topics

- size of expedition
- Chinese goods traded
- places visited

Questions To Ask Zheng He:

1. How many ships and people did you usually take on your expeditions?

2. What Chinese goods did you take to trade?

3. What lands did you visit on your seven voyages?

Zheng He's Answers:

1. The number of vessels varied from about 50 to over 300; at least 27,000 people usually accompanied me.

2. We took along Chinese porcelain, silk, and horses.

3. We traveled to Southeast Asia, and India, to the entrances of the Red Sea and the Persian Gulf, and to East Africa.

THINKING CRITICALLY:
Plan a trading expedition today. Write a paragraph that answers the following questions. What U.S. goods would you take on your expedition? Why? What countries would you visit? Why? Responses vary.

_____

_____

Events and Their Effects in China and India

Identifying Cause-and-Effect Relationships

◇ Each event given below has a corresponding effect or effects that resulted from it. When the event is given, fill in the effect(s) of that event. When the effect is given, fill in the missing event. The first set is done for you.

Event: Genghis Khan and the Mongols overtake northern China.

▼

Effect: In some places, up to 90 percent of the Chinese population disappears.

Event: Mongols organize a restoration of the Grand Canal.

▼

Effect: Thousands of Chinese are forced to work on the project.

▼

Effect: Peasants rebel, led by Zhu Yuanzhang.

Event: Zhu Yuanzhang establishes the Ming dynasty.

▼

Effect: Great strides are made in economics, culture, agriculture, and government.

Event: Aurangzeb expands the Mogul empire through warfare.

▼

Effect: War shrinks the treasury and destroys Indian lands.

Event: Mumtaz Mahal dies.

▼

Effect: Shah Jahan orders the building of a magnificent mausoleum, the Taj Mahal.

THINKING CRITICALLY: How might events in China have been different if Genghis Khan and the Mongols had not overtaken that country?

Several events in China would never have happened or would have happened differently. For example, in some places up to 90 percent of the Chinese population would not have disappeared; Zhu Yuanzhang would probably not have come to power.

Name _____

The New Empires of China and India

Identifying Main Idea and Details

◇ The great civilizations of China and India experienced major changes in the middle centuries. Complete the chart with the topic, main ideas, and details from the chapter.   Sample answers are provided.

TOPIC: The changing civilizations of China and India

MAIN IDEA # 1:
Outside forces changed both China and India

MAIN IDEA # 2:
The civilizations of China and India had highly-developed technologies.

DETAILS:
Answers include:
- Sultan Mahmud of Ghazni sent an army to invade India and then set up a Muslim state.
- In 1398 Timur the Lame invaded India, ultimately causing India to break up into many small states.
- Kublai Khan conquered southern China. Eventually the peasants rebelled against the Mongols and established the Ming dynasty.

DETAILS:
- Marco Polo told about paper money, water clocks, coal, and other inventions used in China.
- In the Indian city of Agra the Taj Mahal, a great architectural wonder, was built.

THINKING CRITICALLY: How do you think the development of China and India would have been different if they had not been invaded?

Answers will vary, but should include information about how the governments, religions,

and populations of China and India would have differed.

Chapter 12, pages 264–279

Name _____

Gathering and Evaluating Information

Gathering and Evaluating Sources of Information

◇ Before gathering information on a subject, you need to decide what sources will be useful to you. Circle the best response to each of the following questions about sources of information on Japanese history since the end of World War II in 1945.

1. What copyright date should a book on Japanese history have?

a. 1900   b. 1944   (c. after 1990)

2. Which would be the best source of information?

a. an almanac   (b. a recent history of Japan) c. a travel guide

3. Where can you find out about changes in population density in Japan since 1945?

a. a history book   (b. a current atlas)   c. old newspapers

4. Where can you find the name of the current Prime Minister of Japan?

(a. recent newspaper stories) b. a dictionary   c. a current atlas

THINKING CRITICALLY: Suppose you go to Japan to interview people about Japanese history since 1945. List the kinds of people you would interview.

Answers will vary, but might include the following: scholars of Japanese history, current and

past politicians, newspaper and television reporters, representative families.

_____

_____

Name _____

Land and Economy

Understanding Economics—The Importance of Land

◇ The Japanese economy was closely linked to control over land. Answer the following questions about the Japanese economic system at different points in history.

1. What did the Japanese once believe about the economic value of their land? Why?

They believed it was very poor because there is little land for growing crops.

2. Who held the most economic power in feudal Japan? Why?

The shogun held more power than the emperor because he ruled over the daimyo.

3. What was the daimyo's economic basis of the power?

The daimyo ruled over regions of land.

4. How did the daimyo protect their economic power?

They relied upon the samurai class to defend their landholdings.

5. What led the Tokugawa government to close Japan to foreigners?

They wished to prevent Japan from being influenced and colonized by European countries.

THINKING CRITICALLY: Using Japan's period of isolation as an example, write a few sentences about the positive and negative effects of a country isolating itself from foreign contact.

Answers will vary, but might mention on the one hand that Japan experienced a period of

great prosperity during its isolation, but on the other hand did not benefit from economic

and cultural exchanges with other countries at the same time.

Name _____

Famous Places, Famous People

Identifying Details; Conducting an Interview

◇ Japan's history is marked by events linked to remarkable people or to magnificent places. Complete the chart below by writing the name of the person, people, or place connected to the events listed on the right.

Person/Place	Event
Nara	first capital of Japan
Lady Murasaki Shikibu	wrote *The Tale of Genji*
Heian-Kyo	poetry contests, elaborate ceremonies
Yoritomo	named first shogun
Mongols	destroyed by a kamikaze
47 Ronin	revenged their master's death

THINKING CRITICALLY: Suppose you could interview one person from Japan's past. Write a list of questions you would ask that person about his or her life and accomplishments.

Answers will vary. _____

_____

_____

Name _____

The Land of the Rising Sun

Summarizing the Chapter

◇ Japan has a long and complex history. Complete the chart below with two facts that support the statement in each box. Sample answers are provided.

The Japanese have alternately welcomed and rejected foreign contact.	After the decline of the emperor's power, the Japanese developed a warrior society.
They were visited by Koreans in 552.	A feudal system developed, closely
Tokugawa Ieyasu closed Japan to most	resembling European feudalism.
foreigners in 1639.	Daimyo ruled over regions, supported by
	armies of samurai.

Japan

Martial arts were developed as spiritual exercises.	The arts have been central to Japanese culture.
Jujitsu involves handholds used to throw an	At Heian-kyo, the imperial court centered
adversary off balance.	around the appreciation of beauty.
Kendo was developed as a way to practice	Noh, Bunraku, and Kabuki have been
sword skills.	popular forms of dramas for centuries.

THINKING CRITICALLY: What aspect of Japanese history or culture interests you most? Explain your choice.

Answers will vary.

_____

Chapter 13, pages 286–301

Developing Visual Literacy

Acquiring Information from Art

◇ Studying art is another way to "read" about the past and present. Circle the correct answers to these questions about the statue on page 322.

1. What general impression does this statue give?

    a. ceremony   b. emotion   c. action ⬭

2. What does the Maya ballplayer seem to be wearing?

    a. religious clothes   b. protective clothing ⬭   c. work clothes

3. What does the Maya ballplayer seem to be doing?

    a. running and talking   b. waiting and looking ⬭   c. stopping and praying

4. What does the Maya ballplayer seem to be looking at?

    a. a ball in the air ⬭   b. players on the field   c. spectators in their seats

5. What do you think the statue would do next if it were alive?

a. stop and rest   b. run after the ball ⬭   c. talk to another player

THINKING CRITICALLY:

Write a paragraph about the Maya ballplayer. Include what he was doing before the moment captured in the statue and what he will be doing after that moment.

Answers will vary.

_____

_____

_____

_____

Name _____

Economics of Trade and Farming

Evaluating Economies

◇ Answer the following questions about the economies of early civilizations in Central and South America.

1. What were the social and economic systems of the Maya? The Maya lived in cities with trade routes connecting different regions.

2. What kinds of goods did the Maya trade? They traded pottery, chocolate, herbs, salt, cotton and cotton cloth.

3. How did the Aztecs build an economy in a difficult physical environment? They built chinampas, or floating gardens, on which they could grow crops.

4. How did the Olmec and Maya calendar help their economies? They could use the calendar to know when to plant and harvest crops.

5. How did Tenochtitlán serve as the center of economic life for Aztecs? Its markets attracted people from the region to buy and sell goods.

THINKING CRITICALLY: What dates or times of the year are important for buying and selling in the economy of the United States?

Answers will vary. Examples: holiday shopping season; seasonal harvests.

_____

_____

Name _____

Different People, Different Cultures

Identifying Details that Support Main Ideas

◇ Each of the early civilizations listed below had distinctive features.
Complete the graphic organizer by listing features for each civilization.

Olmecs
sculptured huge stone heads

survived for 800 years

vanished mysteriously

The Maya
used mathematics system with a zero

built cities

traded actively

Incas
built castles and temples

had sophisticated mathematical and

medical knowledge

Toltecs
built pyramids in Teotihuacán

were ruled by a priest-king called

Quetzalcoatl

Aztecs
settled on an island in Lake Texcoco

practiced human sacrifice

fought many wars

THINKING CRITICALLY: Write about a coming-of-age ceremony or practice
in this country that marks the transition from childhood to adulthood.

Answers will vary. _____

_____

_____

Chapter 14, pages 308-313, 319-321

Name _____

Central and South American Empires

Summarizing the Chapter

◇ Each box below has a statement about the early civilizations of Central and South America. Fill in facts to support the main idea in each box. One has been done for you.

Life in Mesoamerican cultures was marked by ritual.

Inca girls went through a ceremony called quicochico.

Aztecs played tlachtli as part of a religious ceremony.

Mesoamerican and South American peoples had advanced knowledge.

The Olmecs and Maya used sophisticated writing systems.

Metalsmiths worked with alloys to make intricate, beautiful objects.

The Toltecs and Aztecs built pyramids.

The city of Tenochtitlán was a remarkable accomplishment.

The Aztecs built a thriving city in a harsh environment.

The city was larger than any city in Europe at that time.

The city had a road system, a canal network, and a huge temple.

THINKING CRITICALLY: The Maya and Aztecs played sports as part of religious ceremonies. Write about how sports events today are like ceremonies and how they affect communities.

Answers will vary. _____

_____

Chapter 14, pages 308–323

Name _____

The Middle Centuries

Here are some new things that I learned in this unit.

_____

_____

_____

_____

I read about and can locate on a map these landforms and bodies of water:

_____

_____

_____

_____

If I could meet one person I read about in this unit, that person would be

_____ because _____

_____.

My favorite activity in this unit was _____

_____.

Name _____

Formulating Generalizations

Understanding Generalizations

◇ Each box below contains a generalization. Indicate whether this generalization is true or false. Then fill in each box with three facts that support your position.

Europeans were not an adventurous group of peoples.

Europeans voyaged over land to Asia for spices and silks.
_____

Europeans discovered a sea route to Asia.
_____

Europeans explored the Americas.
_____

T	F
	✔

The Renaissance was a time of great advances in the sciences.

Sir Isaac Newton formulated the law of gravity.
_____

Leonardo da Vinci invented weapons and tools.
_____

Copernicus proved that the solar system is heliocentric.
_____

T	F
✔	

Renaissance literature is not relevant in the twentieth century.

In the 1960s, Cervantes' novel inspired a musical comedy.
_____

Many films have been made from Shakespeare's plays.
_____

Machiavelli's *The Prince* continues to provoke controversy.
_____

T	F
	✔

THINKING CRITICALLY: Do you think the following generalization is true or false? "The United States is a culturally rich country." Write a sentence supporting your conclusion.

Answers will vary.
_____

_____

Chapter 15, pages 330–331, 340–347

Economic Change—
Causes and Effects

Identifying and Evaluating Economic Change

◇ Between 1400 and 1700, Europe experienced profound economic changes. Fill in the blanks below with the economic effects associated with the event, trend, or people listed. The first answer is provided.

1. Event: The plague With fewer workers, people were forced to find ways to work

more efficiently and productively.

2. Trend: The demand for art Wealthy people paid artists and sculptors to produce art

for their pleasure.

3. People: The middle class Kings relied on loans and taxes from the middle class to fund

governments and wars.

4. People: Women The chief role of women was domestic, though some women

contributed to the commercial economy.

5. Trend: The Columbian Exchange The flow of goods between Europe and the

Americas brought changes in lifestyle to people in both Europe and the Americas.

THINKING CRITICALLY: Review your answer for question 1. List some positive and negative results of that effect.

Answers will vary. Positive effects could include that working conditions improved.

Negative effects include that people spent more time working, a trend that continues

today. As a result, people have less time to do other things.

Name _____

A Global View of the Renaissa

Identifying Main Ideas; Conducting an Interview

◇ Complete the chart below by listing three important people in each field indicated. List a work or event associated with each person.

Religion

Martin Luther, the Reformation

John Calvin, Calvinism

Catherine de' Medici, St. Bartholomew's

Day Massacre

Sciences

Nicolaus Copernicus, the heliocentric

solar system

Galileo Galilei, telescope

Blaise Pascal, mathematics

Arts

Michelangelo, St. Peter's Church

Rembrandt van Rijn, portraits

Donatello, sculptures

Literature

Miguel de Cervantes, *Don Quixote de*

la Mancha

Niccolò Machiavelli, *The Prince*

William Shakespeare, dramas

THINKING CRITICALLY: Suppose you could interview one of the people you listed above. Whom would you choose and what questions would you ask?

Answers will vary.

_____

_____

_____

_____

Chapter 15, pages 336–349

Name _____

The Rise of Modern Europe

Summarizing the Chapter

◇ The chart below gives the main ideas of the chapter. Fill in the chart with details that support each main idea. The first one in each section has been done for you.

Changes

Many aspects of life in Europe changed dramatically.

Religious protests led to violence and reform.
_____

Scholars reintroduced the cultural heritage of Greece and Rome.
_____

Gutenberg's invention made books more widely available.
_____

New Horizons

Europeans explored new scientific and intellectual worlds.

Copernicus and Galileo studied the planets and stars.
_____

Rembrandt painted non-religious subjects with great skill.
_____

Shakespeare invented hundreds of new words and expressions.
_____

Nationalism

European countries gradually transformed into nations.

Its victory over the Spanish Armada made England a force to be reckoned with.
_____

Louis XIV held absolute power in France, but drained his country's resources.
_____

Peter the Great ordered many reforms in Russia and built St. Petersburg.
_____

THINKING CRITICALLY: Select one of the sentences you wrote above and explain why the event or person was important.

Answers will vary.
_____

_____

Name _____

Summarizing Information

Summarizing

◇ Read the passage and summarize it. First, write a title for your summary. Then write the main idea for each paragraph.

Native Americans produced many foods and other goods. They included turkeys, new types of medicinal plants, a new type of cotton, tobacco, rubber, moccasins, toboggans, and snowshoes. These items were unknown in other regions of the world.

After contact with the Americas, European explorers brought these Native American foods and other goods back to Spain, Portugal, and France. These items then spread to other parts of Europe and eventually to the rest of the world.

One of the greatest Native American contributions was the variety of plants used for food. Native Americans cultivated hundreds of plants. Of those plants more than 50 are of great significance as food products throughout the world. People on all continents now enjoy maize (corn), beans, potatoes, sweet potatoes, and many others.

Title: Sample answer: Native American Contributions

Summary: Sample answer: Native Americans produced foods and goods unknown in

other regions of the world. These items were brought to Europe by explorers and

eventually spread to other parts of the world. A major contribution of Native Americans is

the variety of foods now enjoyed throughout the world.

THINKING CRITICALLY: Summarizing can help you to study and learn new things. What are some other ways that you can use summarizing in everyday life?

Sample answers: to tell friends the plot of a movie, TV show, or book; to discuss an

interesting magazine article; to tell someone what you did during a vacation

_____

_____

Name _____

Forced Labor

Understanding Economic Systems

◇ When Europeans colonized the Americas, they discovered great resources that would make them rich. First, though, they had to set up a system of cheap labor. Answer the questions below.

1. How many people were living in Spanish America when the Europeans first arrived? How many Native Americans lived there by the 1600s?

50 million people; number dropped down to 4 million by the 1600s

2. Why did so many Native Americans die?

They died from mistreatment, overwork, and disease.

3. As the Native American population declined, what did the Europeans do to increase the work force?

They brought in people from Africa as slave labor.

4. Why did the Europeans use slave labor instead of hiring workers for wages?

Slave labor was cheaper, so the Europeans had more profits.

5. How was the peonage system similar to slavery?

Colonists lent money to workers and then forced them to work until the debt was paid.

THINKING CRITICALLY: How was the treatment of Native Americans and Africans as workers alike and different?

Sample answer: Both were forced to work for others. Africans were bought and sold as

slaves, but Native Americans were not. Slavery of Africans went from one generation to the

next. Under the peonage system, Native American workers were trapped by debts that

were inherited by the next generation.

Chapter 16, pages 358–363

Name _____

Peoples of the Americas

Understanding Stated Facts and Details

◇ Complete the chart below with information about Native American peoples, where they lived, and what they did. Sample answers are provided.

PEOPLE	WHERE THEY LIVED	WHAT THEY DID
Anasazi	present-day Arizona, New Mexico, Utah, Colorado	built homes in sides of cliffs; hunted and gathered, then farmed
Comanches	present-day Texas and New Mexico	lived on North American plains; hunted buffalo; became skilled horseback riders
Mound Builders	present-day Georgia, Texas, Ohio, Illinois	built mounds as burial sites and artwork
Hopewell	present-day Ohio and Illinois	created sculptures; traveled to trade goods to use in artwork

THINKING CRITICALLY: The introduction of agriculture had a great impact on the way of life of the Anasazi, and the introduction of the horse changed life for many Native Americans. Write about a development, invention, or other change that has greatly impacted the way people live in the twentieth century.

Answers will vary. _____

_____

_____

Name _____

Changing Cultures in the Americas

Summarizing the Chapter

◇ For each lesson, write a sentence expressing the main idea. Then write a brief summary of the chapter. Sample answers are provided.

Lesson	Summary Sentence
1. A Hemisphere Transformed	Latin American culture developed from a blending of European, Native American, and African cultures.
2. Fall of Great Empires	Cortés conquered the Aztecs; Pizarro conquered the Incas.
3. The French in the Americas	French explored many parts of North America and the Caribbean.
4. Native American Cultures	Native Americans lived in North America for thousands of years and left remnants of their cultures.
5. Sailing the Spanish Main	Spanish fleets carried riches from the Americas to Spain and were sometimes attacked by pirates.

Chapter Summary:
The Spaniards, Portuguese, and French began to explore and colonize the Americas. Native American societies were conquered and crushed, but new cultures grew from the mixture of European, Native American, and African cultures.

THINKING CRITICALLY: Music, art, food, religion, and architecture in the United States have been influenced by Native American, European, and African cultures. Give some examples.

Answers will vary.

_____

_____

Name _____

Classifying Information

Classifying; Understanding Charts

◇ Review pages 386 and 387 in your textbook. Then classify the information on those pages by filling in the chart below.

Country	Date Independence Won	Colonized by This Country/Countries	Independence Leaders
Philippines	July 4, 1946	Spain/United States	Emilio Aguinaldo
Indonesia	1949 (except for western New Guinea—1963)	The Netherlands	Sukarno, Muhammad Hatta
Burma (Myanmar)	January 1948	Great Britain	The Thirty Heroes
Singapore	1959 and 1965	Great Britain	N/A
Vietnam	1954	France	Ho Chi Minh

THINKING CRITICALLY: Now that you have classified the information contained in Lesson 2, what generalizations can you make about these nations of Southeast Asia? In other words, what do the nations have in common?

These nations were colonies of Spain, the United States, the Netherlands, Great Britain, or

France. They all gained their independence between 1946 and 1965. Most had one or more

leaders who helped their country gain independence.

_____

_____

Trade in Southeast Asia

Understanding Trading Patterns in Southeast Asia

◇ Read the statements below. Then, on the map, label important areas in Southeast Asian trade in ancient times. The first has been done for you.

• The narrow strait between the Malay Peninsula and the island of Sumatra became the heart of early trading empires.

• Srivijaya was the first of these empires.

• Palembang, the capital of Srivijaya, served as an exchange point for cargoes from China and India.

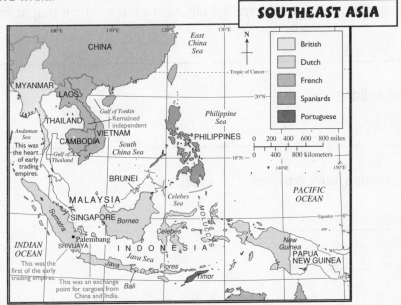

SOUTHEAST ASIA

Now use colored pencils to show which European countries controlled various areas of Southeast Asia. Create a key that explains your colors.

THINKING CRITICALLY: How did geography and natural resources influence trade in ancient Southeast Asia?

Because of its central location, Southeast Asia was a natural trading post for traders

traveling between India and China. The natural resources of Southeast Asia provided the

raw materials to make products for trade, such as palm mats and tortoise-shell jewelry.

Name _____

People Shaping History

Evaluating; Comparing and Contrasting

◇ Read the following quotations. Decide what person in Chapter 17 might have made each statement, and write who might say the words.

1. "I declare that the Philippines is an independent nation."

Emilio Aguinaldo
_____

2. "My father taught me the art of wayang kulit, as his father once taught him."

dalang
_____

3. "I live in a wat in Bangkok."

a Buddhist monk
_____

4. "My ancestor, Rama I, built Bangkok 200 years ago."

the king of Thailand
_____

5. "It is my destiny to rule Burma."

Aung San Suu Kyi
_____

THINKING CRITICALLY: How has Aung San Suu Kyi's life been similar to her father's? How has it been different?

Both Suu and her father fought for Burma's independence. Both were punished for their
_____

beliefs, Aung San by being assassinated and Suu by being confined to her home. Suu,
_____

however, has received international recognition and a chance to continue her fight for
_____

Myanmar's independence. Suu also was educated outside of Myanmar and worked in New
_____

York at the United Nations.
_____

Chapter 17, pages 386–395

Name _____

Civilizations of Southeast Asia

Summarizing the Chapter

◆ Follow the directions to complete the chart.

1. List four art forms that can be found in Southeast Asia today.

shadow plays, Balinese dancing, batik,

gamelan

2. Write two sentences that tell how geography and climate influenced Southeast Asia.

The island nature of the region made it

possible for small, isolated communities to

develop their own unique lifestyles. Climate

affected the farming techniques, clothing,

and homes of the Southeast Asian people.

Civilizations of Southeast Asia

3. What things would you see when visiting Bangkok that you might not see in the United States?

river taxis, Buddhist monks, wats,

kite fights, the Grand Palace

4. Tell how Aung San Suu Kyi was both punished and rewarded for her efforts toward Myanmar's independence.

Suu was punished by being kept under

house arrest, but she was rewarded by

being awarded the Nobel Peace Prize.

THINKING CRITICALLY: Write a sentence that summarizes Chapter 17.

The countries of Southeast Asia were taken over in the 1800s and had to struggle to

regain their independence, but since that time they have combined ancient traditions and

modern lifestyles to become increasingly successful.

Name _____

Recognizing Word Origins

Understanding Etymology

◇ Read about the origins of the words below and then follow the directions or answer the questions.

1. *Luau* is a Hawaiian word that means a feast. Use it in a sentence.

Sample answer: After the plane landed in Hawaii, we were invited to a luau.

_____

2. *Tomato* is a word used by the Nahuatl, a Native American people. What does the origin of the name suggest about this vegetable?

The word origin suggests that tomatoes originally came from the Americas.

_____

3. *Judo* is a Japanese word that comes from words meaning "weakness" and "art." It now describes a kind of self-defense or martial arts. Make a guess as to how the word came to have this meaning.

In judo a weaker person can use the strength of a stronger attacker to defend himself or

herself.

THINKING CRITICALLY:
The French are very worried that their language will be flooded with foreign words as the nations of the world become more interdependent. Should English speakers be worried about this too? Explain your thoughts.

Sample answer: English speakers should not be worried about foreign words entering their

language. English has always had many words borrowed from other cultures.

_____

_____

Name _____

Mercantilism

Understanding Global Trading Patterns

◇ **Answer the questions below about trading around the globe.**

1. According to the mercantile theory, what would happen to other countries if one nation grew wealthier?

The other countries would become poorer.

2. Why was trade important to the mercantile theory?

According to the mercantile theory, trade was one way for a country to take wealth from

other countries.

3. How could a country have a favorable balance of trade?

by selling more products to other countries than it bought from them

4. How did governments try to discourage people from buying imported goods?

Governments discouraged the buying of imports by placing special taxes on them to make

imports more costly than products made in the home country.

5. Why were colonies important to the mercantile theory?

Colonies allowed economic exploitation. They provided a cheap source of raw materials

and a new market for finished goods.

THINKING CRITICALLY: Was the mercantile assumption about wealth true or false? Explain your reasoning.

Sample answer: This assumption about wealth was false, because new wealth was continually

being found in the form of new supplies of gold and silver. Wealth was also being made in

the form of value that was added to raw materials when they were made into goods.

Chapter 18, pages 402–405

Name _____

Colonies and Colonizers

Understanding Stated Facts and Details

◇ After each place listed below, tell which European country or countries had colonies in it. Then answer the questions that follow.

Africa — Britain, France, Portugal, Belgium, Spain, Germany, Italy, Netherlands (Dutch)

India — Great Britain, Portugal

New Zealand — Great Britain

Canada — France, Great Britain

South America — Spain, Portugal, France, Netherlands

China — Portugal, Great Britain

East Indies — Netherlands

Southeast Asia — France

Egypt — Great Britain

West Indies — Netherlands, France

I. Why did few Portuguese move to Portugal's colonies?

Portugal was small and had very few people to start with, so it could not send many

people to other lands.

2. Why did few French move to France's colonies?

Few French people were willing to swap a comfortable life in France for a rugged life in

the colonies.

THINKING CRITICALLY: Colonizers generally thought colonies existed only to make them rich. What problems might this attitude cause?

Sample answer: The people whose land was taken over by the colonizers would feel

exploited and angry at the colonizers. This might lead to uprisings, war, and someday even

the loss of the colony.

Name _____

The Age of Imperialism

Summarizing the Chapter

◇ Fill in the chart below by listing two examples each in boxes 1 through 3. In box 4, write a sentence summarizing what the chapter says about the topic. Sample answers are provided.

1. Industrial Revolution: New Inventions

Steam engines _____

Machines to produce goods _____

3. Borrowing from Other Lands

Tea _____

Words from foreign lands _____

mperialism: New Colonies

Dutch take the East _____

es. _____

n build the _____

ld's largest empire. _____

EUROPEAN NATIONS AND IDEAS EXPAND

4. The Great Exhibition: A New Vision of the World

Some people believed that the Industrial Revolution _____

would lead people to compete to make better _____

products rather than fight wars. _____

THINKING CRITICALLY: Considering what you have read about the effects of the Industrial Revolution, would you say it was a bad thing or a good thing?

Answers will vary. Sample answer: The Industrial Revolution was both good and bad. It led

to suffering such as child labor and unemployment. However, it also led to trade links

around the world.

Chapter 18, pages 402–417

Name _____

Global Expansion

This is a list of some new facts that I learned in this unit.

_____

_____

_____

_____

Now I can locate these nations of Southeast Asia on a map.

_____   _____

_____   _____

If I could visit any place that I read about in this unit, I would travel to

_____

_____.

The most interesting part of this unit was learning about

_____

_____.

Unit 4, Chapters 15, 16, 17, 18

Recognizing Fact and Opinion

Distinguishing Fact from Opinion

◇ **Write your answers to these questions in complete sentences.**
Sample answers are provided.

1. Find one fact and one opinion in Chapter 19, and write them below.

Fact: Sample answer: In 1917 the Russian people rose up against their czar.

Opinion: Sample answer: In some ways nationalism was a good idea.

2. For each item you listed in question 1, explain how you determined whether it is a fact or an opinion.

Fact: Sample answer: This statement can be shown to be a fact by the historical accounts of

the Russian Revolution.

Opinion: Sample answer: This statement describes what the author thinks about

nationalism.

3. How could you rewrite the above fact to make it an opinion?

Sample answer: The most important moment in Russian history was when the Russian

people rose up in 1917.

THINKING CRITICALLY: Choose a topic from Chapter 19 and write your opinion about it. Then list two facts that support your opinion.

Sample answer: Opinion—Women reformers were brave. Facts—They stood up to men

who didn't want them to have equal rights. They struggled and campaigned for the right to

vote.

_____

Name _____

Equal Rights = Equal Pay?

Understanding Women's Role in the Economy

◇ **Fill in the blanks to complete the sentences.**

1. Women in the nineteenth century were expected to contribute to the economy by

raising children, cooking, and keeping house. _____

2. Some poor working women were against equal rights because they were worried

about earning enough money to survive. _____

3. Women such as Sample answers: Florence Nightingale and Elizabeth Blackwell

were leaders and pioneers because they broke into professions that had been

traditionally male-dominated.

4. World War II was an important event in the history of women's rights because

women proved they could become skilled factory workers. _____

_____

5. In my opinion, Sample answer: new laws must be passed

so that women are finally ensured equal pay for equal work.

Thinking Critically: If you did not have the right to choose your work or profession, what would you do about it? Write your plan of action.

Sample answers: demonstrating for the right, calling senator or representative, holding a

conference

_____

_____

Name _____

World Happenings

Identifying Cause-and-Effect Relationships

◇ Create your own quiz game by writing questions (Q) and answers (A) about nations and events in each category. One question has been provided for you.

Categories	Q&A #1	Q&A #2	Q&A #3
Conflicts	Q: What war was the result of nationalism in 1914? A: World War I	Q: What conflict is associated with the guillotine? A: The French Revolution	Q: During what conflict did the genocide of Jewish people occur? A: World War II
Nations	Q: What country was formed after a revolution against Great Britain? A: United States	Q: What country fought Spain for its independence? A: Mexico	Q: What nations were created by the division of empires after World War I? A: Poland, Czechoslovakia, Yugoslavia, Finland, Estonia, Latvia and Lithuania, Turkey

THINKING CRITICALLY: How might history be different if a dictator such as Hitler had not come to power?

Sample answers: Another dictator might have come to power because of the problems in

Germany. Or: World War II and the Holocaust might not have occurred without Hitler.

Chapter 19, pages 426–441

Name _____

The Spread of Nationalism

Summarizing the Chapter

◇ In the chart below list main ideas found in each of the first four lessons in the chapter that help explain the spread of nationalism. (Hint: Read the Focus statements to help you.) Sample answers are provided.

NATIONS IN CONFLICT

1. Growth in wealth and military power led to feelings of nationalism.

2. Many nations in Europe experienced internal upheavals and social changes.

REVOLUTIONARY TIMES

1. Citizens deprived of basic rights may revolt against their government.

2. Revolutions occurred in several countries between 1775 and 1921.

RISE OF DICTATORSHIP

1. After World War I, many European countries experienced economic depression.

2. Powerful leaders were able to take over weakened governments.

WORLD WARS I AND II

1. The forces of nationalism and imperialism led to World Wars I and II.

2. New technology made World Wars I and II the bloodiest conflicts in history.

THINKING CRITICALLY: Do you think nationalism is helpful or hurtful to the nations of the world?

Answers will vary. Sample answer: Nationalism can be helpful when it encourages people

to help their fellow citizens. It can be hurtful when it leads people to become aggressive.

Chapter 19, pages 426–445

Name _____

Reading Resource Maps

Understanding Special-Purpose Maps

◇ Use the map on page 461 of your textbook to answer the questions below.

1. What is the purpose of the map? What specific information does it provide?

The map shows the economic resources of Latin America. It shows which resources are

available in each country.

2. According to the map, which Latin American countries produce coffee?

El Salvador, Costa Rica, Haiti, Colombia, and Brazil produce coffee.

3. When you enjoy a cup of hot chocolate or a chocolate bar, which Latin American country may have provided a key ingredient of your treat?

Grenada produces cocoa.

4. In which Latin American countries would you be most likely to find factories? Why?

Mexico, Costa Rica, Panama, Colombia, Peru, Bolivia, Chile, Argentina, Uruguay,

Brazil, Venezuela, St. Lucia, Puerto Rico, Antigua, and Barbuda probably have

factories because these countries are involved in manufacturing.

THINKING CRITICALLY: Books, maps, globes, and bulletin boards are all resources in a classroom. Create a map of your classroom that shows where different resources are located.

Name _____

Latin American Food Production

Understanding the Economics of Trade

◇ Use the map on page 461 and the chart on page 462 to answer the questions.

1. List the types of food products grown in Latin American countries.

sugar, bananas, corn, vegetables, grain, coffee, cocoa, spices

2. How does Latin America's production of coffee compare with its production of

wheat? Why? Latin America produces 62 percent of the world's coffee and only 3 percent

of the world's wheat. Latin America's climate is better suited to growing coffee than wheat.

3. What conditions are necessary for successful trade of food products?

climate, work force, transportation, communication

4. Why does the United States import Central American coffee and bananas?

These crops don't grow well in most of the United States.

THINKING CRITICALLY: Why are diamonds, emeralds, and sapphires so valuable? How is trading for food different from trading for jewels?

Sample answer: Jewels are valuable because they are often rare and because people like to

decorate themselves with jewelry. Precious stones have been symbols of status and wealth

for centuries. People trade for food because they need food to live. They trade for jewels

because they want them.

Name _____

Latin America

Understanding Stated Facts and Details

 Fill in the information about Latin America's independence movement.

Main Idea of Lesson 1:

Latin America struggled for independence from European influence. _____

_____

Important People

Pierre Toussaint L'Ouverture, Father Miguel Hidalgo, Simón Bolívar, José de San Martín,

Benito Juárez, José Martí _____

Important Events

Slave revolt in Haiti, Mexican Independence, liberation of Venezuela, Monroe Doctrine,

Cuban independence from Spain _____

Important Places

Haiti, Mexico City, Venezuela, Argentina, Cuba, Puerto Rico _____

_____

THINKING CRITICALLY: Why do you think people struggle so hard for

independence? Why is it important?

Sample answers: to make better lives for themselves; to take control of their own lives; to

maintain their own culture

Chapter 20, pages 452–459

Name _____

The Nations of Latin America

Summarizing the Chapter

◇ For each lesson, write a sentence that gives the main idea.

Independence and Its Consequences

Latin American countries had to fight for independence from European countries.

They Led the Way

L'Overture, Bolívar, de San Martín, Juárez, and Martí all led independence movements.

Latin American Economies

Latin America has many natural resources, but what it trades depends on geography

and the skills of its workers.

Immigrants in Latin America

Immigrants in Latin America contributed toward building its economy and culture.

The Life of a Gaucho

Gauchos led an independent life riding the range.

THINKING CRITICALLY: What are some characteristics or qualities that leaders of the independence movements might have had?

Answers will vary, but might include devotion to their cause, willingness to take risks, and

the ability to inspire or lead people.

Chapter 20, pages 452–469

Name _____

Comparing Graphs

Understanding and Comparing Bar Graphs

◇ Use the bar graphs below to answer the questions that follow.

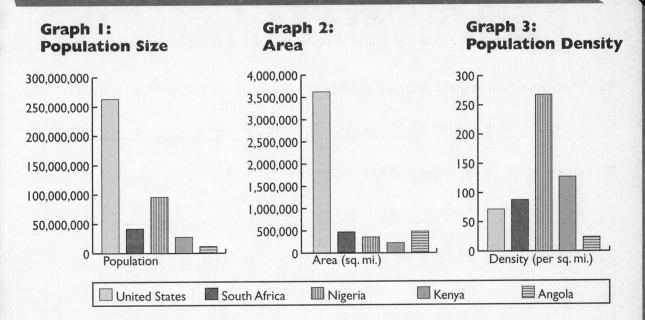

**Graph 1:
Population Size**

**Graph 2:
Area**

**Graph 3:
Population Density**

Population

Area (sq. mi.)

Density (per sq. mi.)

☐ United States ■ South Africa ▥ Nigeria ▨ Kenya ▤ Angola

1. Rank the countries in order of their population size: United States, Nigeria,

South Africa, Kenya, Angola

2. Which country ranks first in population density but second in population size?

Nigeria

3. Use the graphs to compare the area, population, and population density of South

Africa and Kenya. South Africa has a larger area and population than Kenya, while Kenya

has a greater population density than South Africa.

THINKING CRITICALLY: Using the information provided in the graphs, write a
statement about two of the countries represented.

Answers will vary.

Name _____

Europe and Africa

Applying Economic Knowledge

◇ The history of Africa since the fifteenth century is deeply rooted in economic interests. Answer the following questions about the way economics has affected Africa.

1. What were two major reasons for European involvement in Africa?

European nationalism and the slave trade were two major reasons.

2. What impact did the Industrial Revolution have on Africa?

It drove Europeans in search of new markets for their goods.

3. What are four factors that led European countries to colonize Africa?

Natural resources, political power, prestige, money

4. Why did African countries not gain independence until late in the twentieth century?

The colonial powers were reluctant to give up the wealth these countries supplied them with.

5. What are two economic effects of the policy of apartheid in South Africa?

Apartheid deprived many blacks of economic opportunities; and it inspired an international

boycott on trade with South Africa.

THINKING CRITICALLY: How do you think that other nations' refusal to trade with South Africa affected its economy?

Answers should reflect that it had a negative effect on South Africa's economy.

_____

_____

_____

Chapter 21, pages 476–481

Name _____

Leading Africa to Freedom

Understanding Main Ideas; Writing a Diary Entry

◇ The chart below lists three notable Africans. Fill in the places and events with which these people are associated, as well as the outcomes of those events.

Person/People	Place	Event(s)	Outcome
Shaka Zulu	Zulu nation	Mfecane ("smashing up")	Expansion of Zulu empire
Nelson Mandela	South Africa	Apartheid, Mandela imprisoned	Mandela is released, elected president
Kwame Nkrumah	Gold Coast	Positive Action protests	Gold Coast wins independence as Ghana

THINKING CRITICALLY: Suppose you are Jomo Kenyatta. Choose a major event or period in his life and write a diary entry from his perspective.

Answers will vary.

_____

_____

_____

_____

Name _____

Independence In Africa

Summarizing the Chapter

◇ Write in two facts that support the main idea in each box.

Enslaving Africa

Europeans sold millions of Africans into slavery.

Landowners in the Americas and the Caribbean needed labor.

Europeans enlisted Africans to take part in the capture of people for slavery.

Colonizing Africa

European countries divided up most of Africa into colonies.

European countries wanted markets for their goods.

Industrializing nations wanted Africa's natural resources.

Liberating Africa

Many African nations gained independence only in the late 1900s.

There were both violent and peaceful protests.

Freedom spread through Africa after Ghana became independent.

THINKING CRITICALLY: What qualities do you think leaders such as Nelson Mandela and Jomo Kenyatta have in common?

Answers will vary but may include commitment to their cause and leadership qualities that

attract others to their cause.

Chapter 21, pages 476–493

Making an Outline

Making Outlines

◇ Use pages 500–503 in your book to complete the outline below.

THE OTTOMAN EMPIRE

I. Rise of the Empire

    A. Turks conquered people in the Middle East. _____

    B. Boundaries extend from central Europe to Greece. _____

II. Outside Influences
    A. Domination by Europe

        1. Napoleon conquers Egypt. _____

        2. Europe's economy is stronger. _____

    B. Western culture spreads and weakens the empire. _____

III. Carving up the Empire

    A. European ideas of nationalism spread. _____

    B. People in the empire revolted against high taxes. _____

    C. Difference of religion between groups caused revolts. _____

THINKING CRITICALLY: What devices in your textbook work like an outline to help you organize and understand information?

The heads and sub-heads are like the categories in an outline. They help to organize the

information into smaller chunks and show the logical structure of the chapter. Paragraphs

also divide the text into meaningful units.

Name _____

Europe and the Middle East

Comparing Economies

◇ Compare the European and Middle Eastern economies in the nineteenth century by filling in the Venn diagram. Write about agriculture, industrialization, and trade. Sample answers are provided.

European

Expanding agriculture and _____

population _____

Industrial Revolution _____

Exports around the world _____

Greater quantities, lower _____

prices _____

Both

Make goods

from cotton

and silk

Middle Eastern

Slower growth _____

Produce cotton and silk _____

Smaller quantities, higher prices _____

Farmers dependent on _____

European buyers _____

_____

THINKING CRITICALLY: Summarize how the nations of Europe used the advances of the Industrial Revolution to expand their economies.

Sample answer: During the Industrial Revolution, European factories produced goods very

quickly and cheaply. Europeans bought raw materials from all over—including the Middle

East—and transformed them into finished goods. These goods could then be sold around

the world for large profits.

Chapter 22, pages 500–501

Name _____

Middle Eastern Events

Placing Events in Proper Sequence

◇ On the line after each event, write the date of the event. Then write 1–9 on the lines before the events to place them in order.

_2_ Greece wins independence from the Ottoman Empire. _1827_

_6_ Golda Meir becomes prime minister of Israel. _1969_

_1_ Napolean invades Egypt. _1798_

_3_ Suez canal opens. _1869_

_8_ Persian Gulf War is fought. _1991_

_4_ Great Britain invades Egypt. _1882_

_5_ Israel becomes a nation. _1948_

_7_ Camp David Accords. _1979_

_9_ Rabin and Arafat sign peace treaty. _1993_

THINKING CRITICALLY: Suppose you could interview one of the people involved in the Camp David Accords or the peace treaty signed in 1993. What person would you choose, and what questions would you ask?

Answers will vary.

_____

_____

_____

_____

_____

Name _____

The Middle East in Modern Ti

Summarizing the Chapter

◇ Make an outline of the chapter. Write the chapter title and then each lesson title. Write two important points for each lesson. The first lesson has been done for you. Sample answers are provided.

Title: The Middle East in Modern Times

I. Changing Life in the Middle East

   A. Europe spreads into the

    Middle East.

   B. Middle Eastern countries gain

    independence.

II. New Nations from an Old Empire

   A. Many new nations are created.

   B. Turkey takes on Western ways.

III. Changing Roles of Women

   A. Women seek freedom and rights.

   B. Women leaders gain positions.

IV. Unrest in the Middle East

   A. Lebanon is divided by religion.

   B. Iraq and Iran go to war.

V. Bridging the Gap

   A. Israel becomes a nation.

   B. PLO gains Palestinian self-rule.

THINKING CRITICALLY: Think of some ways for people in the Middle East to get along and settle their differences. Write your ideas below.

Answers will vary.

_____

_____

_____

_____

Chapter 22, pages 500–517

Drawing Conclusions

Drawing Conclusions

 Read the paragraph. Write down the selection information and the known information. Then make a conclusion. Sample answers are provided.

Mohandas K. Gandhi was born on October 2, 1869. His mother practiced Jainism, a religion that emphasizes nonviolence and vegetarianism. When Gandhi was a boy, he sometimes ate meat with his friends, but he felt very guilty about going against his mother's beliefs. When he became a man, Gandhi was a great leader who used peaceful protest to make social change. He led strikes and demonstrations. He started boycotts of British products. He practiced civil disobedience. But he never used violence to express his political beliefs.

Selection Information

Gandhi's mother practiced Jainism.

Jainism emphasizes nonviolence and vegetarianism.

As a boy, Gandhi felt guilty about going against his mother's beliefs.

As a man, Gandhi used nonviolent methods to make social change.

+

Known Information

Parents' beliefs often strongly influence those of their children.

=

Conclusion

The religious beliefs of Gandhi's mother had a strong impact on the beliefs and behavior

of her son.

THINKING CRITICALLY: Find a paragraph in Chapter 23 from which you can draw a conclusion. Write the location of the paragraph and your conclusion here.

Answers will vary.

Name _____

Asian Economies

Understanding Economic Systems

◇ A country's economy is based on resources and on goods that are produced and traded for profit. Economies may be based on farms, factories, and industries. Describe the economy of each country below.

Japan many factories to export goods; railroads and port facilities; growth in strength

and wealth since 1950

China farms are communes, not privately owned; farms and small factories are staffed

by peasants; Communist system

Taiwan trade with United States and other countries; economic prosperity

Hong Kong banking and manufacturing; capitalist system

North Korea rich natural resources of coal and iron; farming; state-owned industries; low

wages but free health care and housing; Communist system

South Korea few resources; factories and high-tech industries; textile industry;

manufacturing—cars, ships, steel, computers

THINKING CRITICALLY: Compare the economies of the countries above. In general, how are they alike and different?

Some are Communist, some are capitalist. Most have farms and manufacturing. Some of the

economies have made those countries strong.

Chapter 23, pages 524–529, 532–534

Name _____

Ten Largest Cities

Identifying Cities

◇ Use the map to answer the questions.

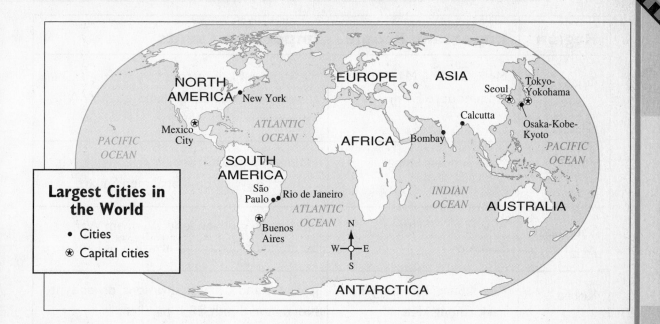

Largest Cities in the World
- Cities
- ✷ Capital cities

1. Of the ten largest cities in the world, how many are located in Asia? five _____

2. Which of the cities are in Japan? Tokyo-Yokohama, Osaka-Kobe-Kyoto

3. Why do you think two of the cities are located in Japan, a country small in area?

Sample answer: Japan is an island nation, so it can't expand outward as its population grows.

THINKING CRITICALLY: Why do you think so many of the world's largest cities are in Asia?

Sample answer: Countries in that part of the world have large populations, so many

people are concentrated in urban areas. The countries also have very old cultures, and

their cities have been existing and growing for centuries.

Name _____

Throughout Asia

Summarizing the Chapter

◇ Complete the chart with information from Chapter 23.

Region	Important People	Important Events
Japan	Meiji, General MacArthur, Commodore Perry	black ships, Meiji restoration, attacked China, annexed Korea, heavily damaged in WWII, Korean war
China	Mao Zedong, Deng Xiaoping, Ci Xi	Opium War, Boxer Rebellion, Long March, Cultural Revolution, Tiananmen Square
Southeast Asia	Norodum Sihanouk, Sukarno	Indonesian independence, Vietnam War, bombing of Cambodia, invasion of Laos
Korea	Kim Il Sung, Kim Jong Il, Park Chung Hee	Japanese and Chinese invasions, divided into North and South, 38th parallel
India	Mohandas Gandhi, Muhammad Ali Jinnah, Jawaharlal Nehru, Indira Gandhi	March to the ocean, boycotts and civil disobedience, independence for India, Pakistan separates, Bangladesh

THINKING CRITICALLY: How do you think China might be different today if Japan had remained an influence there?

Sample answer: China might not have become Communist. Private ownership of land and

factories might not have ended. China might have made technological advances similar to

those in Japan.

_____

_____

Chapter 23, pages 524–539

Name _____

Times of Great Change

Here are some new things that I learned in this unit.

_____

_____

_____

_____

_____

I'd like to learn more about _____

because _____

_____.

In this unit I learned about and can locate these countries on a map.

_____   _____

_____   _____

I think that another name for this unit could be _____

_____.

Name _____

Recognizing Propaganda

Analyzing Propaganda; Writing a Speech

◇ On the chart below are three statements. Complete the chart by inferring what kind of group might support the statement, the group's purpose, and the key words used to convey the group's message.

STATEMENT	GROUP	PURPOSE	KEY WORDS
"Communism is the corruption of a dream of justice."	An anti-communist political organization	To denounce communism as contrary to fairness and equality	corruption, dream, justice
"America, the land of unlimited possibilities."	An American capitalist or politician	To promote the American way of life	unlimited possibilities
"You cannot make a revolution with silk gloves."	A revolutionary or terrorist leader	To justify the use of violence and extreme methods	revolution, silk gloves

THINKING CRITICALLY: Suppose you are a speechwriter. Decide on a group to whom your candidate will be speaking and the purpose of the speech. Write some sentences for a speech. Circle the key words you used to convey your message.

Answers will vary.

_____

_____

_____

_____

_____

The Cold War

Identifying Economic Factors

◇ **Answer these questions about the economic impact of the cold war.**

1. Why did the Americans want to rebuild Europe after World War II?

They wanted to promote democracy in Europe and build markets for Western businesses.

2. What was the economic conflict at the heart of the cold war?

The Americans wanted to have a world economy based on capitalism, while the Soviets

wanted to promote communism.

3. How did the Soviet Union promote communism in the world?

It supported Communist regimes in countries such as China and North Korea.

4. How did workers in Poland contribute to the fall of communism in Europe?

The workers' union called Solidarity protested successfully against the Polish Communist

government.

THINKING CRITICALLY: Why do you think Eastern European countries
embraced Western economic methods after the cold war?

Answers will vary but might include that the countries chose Western economic methods

because they were more successful and provided more opportunities and choice for

individuals.

_____

_____

_____

Name _____

The Cold Race Into Space

Identifying Achievements; Comparing and Assessing Events

◆ The chart below lists some highlights of the space race.
Complete the chart.

PERSON/PEOPLE	EVENT	SIGNIFICANCE
Yuri Gagarin	Flight of Vostok I	First man to fly in space
John Glenn	Flight of Friendship 7	First American to orbit Earth
Neil Armstrong and Buzz Aldrin	Moonlanding in *Apollo 11*	First people to walk on the moon
Soviet cosmonauts and American astronauts	The Apollo-Soyuz Test Project	First combined space mission between the U. S. and U.S.S.R.
Sally Ride	Flight of space shuttle *Challenger*	First American woman in space

THINKING CRITICALLY: Write a paragraph explaining why you think the United States should, or should not, spend money on space exploration.

Answers will vary. _____

_____

_____

_____

Chapter 24, pages 558–559

Tensions of the Cold War

Summarizing the Chapter

◇ The period from 1945 to 1990 was dominated by the cold war, its effect on American values, and the profound changes in the United States during the 1960s. Complete the chart by listing three major events for each category.

THE COLD WAR

The Berlin Wall is built.
_____

The Korean War is fought.
_____

The Hungarian uprising is put down.
_____

_____

AMERICAN VALUES

The Truman Doctrine is
_____

implemented.
_____

The Marshall Plan goes into effect.
_____

The Berlin Airlift takes place.

THE SIXTIES

The Civil Rights Movement
_____

Anti-war protests
_____

Feminist movement begins.
_____

THINKING CRITICALLY: List some things the United States and the Soviet Union might have done to ease tensions during the cold war.

Answers will vary. _____

_____

_____

_____

_____

_____

Chapter 24, pages 548–563

Name _____

Evaluating Arguments

Evaluating Arguments

◇ Read the passage and answer the questions.

In some ways the world is a global village. Technology allows people in many nations to share the same experience. Early television sets had small screens.

In other ways, the world isn't a global village at all. The people in a village work together and support each other. In the world today, however, different cultures often clash, and this can lead to violence. The world is like a village that doesn't get along.

1. In the first paragraph, underline the sentence that doesn't support the argument.

Is the sentence irrelevant or inconsistent? irrelevant _____

2. Write another sentence that supports the argument in the first paragraph.

Sample answer: Through the Internet, someone in China can send an e-mail message to the

United States in seconds.

3. In the second paragraph, underline the sentence that doesn't support the argu-

ment. Is the sentence irrelevant or inconsistent? inconsistent _____

4. Explain why the sentence you underlined in the second paragraph is irrelevant or

inconsistent. Sample answer: It is inconsistent because the first sentence says the world

isn't a global village, and the last one says the world is like a village. The last sentence

doesn't agree with what the first sentence says.

THINKING CRITICALLY: Do you think the world today is or is not a global village? Explain your answer.

Answers will vary.

World Poverty

Understanding Economic Disparities

◇ **Are the fictional people described below from rich nations or poor nations? Place each name under the correct column below.**

For her work, Flora is paid low wages compared to the same work in the United States.

Diego has no choice but to buy imported goods from developed countries.

Samuel's factory is in a developing country, but the profits go to Samuel in his own country.

Jamal will die at age 47; Yukio will live to be 79.

Shandra and millions of other women like her will die of starvation or disease.

RICH NATION	POOR NATION
Samuel	Flora
Yukio	Diego
	Jamal
	Shandra

THINKING CRITICALLY: An estimated 70 percent of the world's poor people are women. Why do you think there are so many more women in poverty than men?

Sample answers: Men own more property; women often have to care for their children as

well as themselves; women do not have the same opportunities to advance in their careers.

Name _____

People in a Global Village

Understanding Stated Facts

◇ For each section of the web, provide the information requested.

GLOBAL CULTURE
Give examples of technology, music, food, and fashion that make it seem as though the world is shrinking.

Concorde jet, fax, Internet

rock music heard everywhere

McDonald's around the world

T-shirts and blue jeans

CONFLICTS
Name three types of conflicts that are happening throughout the world.

a clash of cultures

religious conflicts

differences between ethnic groups

GLOBAL VILLAGE

PEOPLE ON THE MOVE
What is the difference between immigrants and refugees?

Immigrants are often people from developing

countries who move to richer, industrialized

countries in hope of a better life. Refugees

are people who move around because of

war, political unrest, or persecution.

VIOLENCE
Give examples of terrorism and explain why some people use violence this way.

Oklahoma City and World Trade Center

were bombed. Yitzhak Rabin was murdered

and people were gassed in the Tokyo subway.

Extremists use violence to show their power

and to call attention to their point of view.

THINKING CRITICALLY: Why do some countries resist a global culture?

Some feel traditional ways are better. Some countries feel their values have a long history

and don't want their values overtaken by others.

Chapter 25, pages 568–583

The World in Conflict

Summarizing the Chapter

◇ Write a sentence that gives the main idea of the chapter. Then write three details from each lesson. Sample answers are provided.

MAIN IDEA: Instead of wars between countries, there are conflicts of culture,

religion, and ethnic groups within nations.

A Shrinking World

1. Global village

_____

2. People moving

around the world

3. Conflicts over

religion and culture

Problems Living Together

1. Most wars are between ethnic or religious groups.

2. Yugoslavia broke up.

3. Ethnic violence between Serbs and Muslims

Changing Economic Distribution

1. Businesses are worldwide multinational corporations.

2. Headquarters are in developed countries, factories

are in developing countries.

3. 70% of the world's poor people are women.

THINKING CRITICALLY: List some examples of how you are part of a global village. Think about communication, transportation, music, food, and clothing.

Sample responses: Internet, World Wide Web, flying to Europe, wearing clothes made in

other countries, eating ethnic foods, listening to music from around the world

_____

Name _____

Making Predictions

Predicting Outcomes

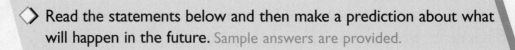

◇ Read the statements below and then make a prediction about what will happen in the future. Sample answers are provided.

1. The number of people in the United States who are over age 65 increased by 100 percent between 1960 and 1994. Experts believe that improved health care will continue to let people live longer.

The number of people over 65 will continue to increase.

2. In the past ten years, the number of adults in the United States who use a computer has doubled. And many people use computers to work out of their homes.

More people will use computers, and more people will work out of their homes.

3. Between 1980 and 1992, the percentage of Americans living in city areas rose from 76 percent to 80 percent. And more areas are becoming citylike as suburbs become more crowded.

In the future, a higher percentage of people will live in city areas.

THINKING CRITICALLY: Suppose a new ethnic group is discovered in a remote part of the South American rain forest. Do you think these people will be left alone or forced to become a part of the modern world? Explain.

Sample answer: They will become a part of the modern world. Nearly all people in the

world have been touched by modern technology and have become a part of the larger

world whether they wanted to or not.

_____

_____

Chapter 26, pages 588–589

Name _____

Cooperation through Technology

Understanding Global Impacts of Technology

◇ Answer the questions below.

1. Name some technologies that have allowed nations to meet and communicate better to solve regional or global problems.

Examples are faster trains and planes and computer technology such as personal
_____

computers, e-mail, fax machines and satellite hookups.
_____

2. Which world organizations have worked to improve world health, and what medical technology has been important in achieving their goals?

The World Health Organization and UNICEF have worked to control disease in the world.
_____

The development of vaccinations was important in achieving their goals.
_____

3. In what ways has the growth of technology hurt the environment, and in what ways has it helped?

Developments in mining and logging have caused roads to be built through the rain forests,
_____

which has caused destruction of the rain forests. Personal computers and e-mail can
_____

reduce the amount of paper people use, which could save valuable forest resources.
_____

THINKING CRITICALLY: What is a problem that you feel needs to be addressed by cooperation between different nations in the world? Propose a new international organization to work on solving the problem. Include who should be involved, and how the organization will work.

Answers will vary.
_____

_____

_____

Name _____

Events That Changed Your Life

Identifying Cause-and-Effect Relationships

◇ Explain the effect that each event below has had on your life. Answers will vary.

EVENT	EFFECT
1. Jet planes were built that cut air travel from days to hours.	I was able to travel to another state on my last vacation.
2. Satellite telephone networks allowed instant communication almost anywhere on earth.	I can call my mom while she is driving home from work.
3. Computers became small enough to fit on a desk.	We can use the computer in the class-room to check information on the Internet.
4. Nations began to cooperate to end diseases.	My friends and I have been healthier without diseases such as measles and diptheria.
5. International groups began to try to save the rain forest.	The air I breathe today is fresher because some parts of the rain forest have been preserved.

THINKING CRITICALLY: If you could create an event that would make the world cooperate and communicate better, what would it be? Why?

Sample answer: I would like to see a message come from another planet in the universe.

Then humans might begin to think of themselves as citizens of the planet Earth, and not as

citizens of separate nations.

The World in Harmony

Summarizing the Chapter

◇ In each section of the chart, list examples that illustrate the topic.

Cooperating as Nations

Nations cooperate on standards for operating planes

IMF works to promote trade

WHO works to end diseases

UN works for peace

A SHRINKING WORLD

Cooperating to Help the Environment

The World Wildlife Fund and the

Environmental Defense Fund have

coordinated efforts to save the rain

forests. The Cousteau Society has

emphasized education.

The World Wide Fund for Nature has

raised money to set up rain forest preserves.

People have recycled and reduced the use

of products from the rain forest.

Technology

Train and plane transport

makes travel time shorter.

Telephone calls are

transmitted by satellite.

Computers allow people

to communicate via the

Internet. Companies

communicate by

videoconferencing.

THINKING CRITICALLY: How are you using knowledge from the past on this very day?

Sample answer: I have been reading a textbook that includes knowledge from the past.

Also, I have used electricity, transportation systems, and modern conveniences that were

discovered or invented in the past.

Name _____

Toward the Twenty-first Century

Here are some of the most interesting things I learned in this unit.

_____

_____

_____

_____

_____

_____

I'd like to learn more about _____

_____.

This is what I discovered about conflicts in the world today.

_____

_____

Here's how I'd like the world of tomorrow to be.

_____

_____